Speech Pathology

with

Methods in Speech Correction

SPEECH PATHOLOGY
With
Methods in Speech Correction

By

Sara M. Stinchfield, Ph.D.
Associate Professor of Psychology
Mount Holyoke College

1928

EXPRESSION COMPANY, PUBLISHERS
BOSTON - MASSACHUSETTS

To My Mother

Alwilda Marston Stinchfield

ACKNOWLEDGMENTS.

The author wishes to make acknowledgments to the following authors or publishers for permission to quote from their publications, or to use poems, or selections.

To Harper & Bros. for use of the poem *May is Building Her House,* by Richard Le Gallienne; to Houghton, Mifflin Co., Boston for use of the following: *East Wind,* by Abby Farwell Brown; excerpts from Longfellow and Lowell, viz: *The Beggar Maid, Robin Hood and Clorinda, The Three Kings, Aladdin, Castles in Spain,* quotations from Oliver Wendall Holmes' *Old Ironsides, The One Horse Shay, Lord of the Universe;* Amy Lowell's *A Sprig of Rosemary;* to C. F. Weber & Co., San Francisco for permission to use the poem *Columbus* by Joaquin Miller; to Charles Scribner's Sons for permission to use, by special arrangement, H. C. Bunner's *One, Two, Three,* to quote from Eugene Field's *The Night Wind,* and for excerpts from R. L. Stevenson's *Where Go the Boats? The Kites, In Winter, The Gingham Dog and the Calico Cat, The Friendly Cow;* to Jeannette Marks of Mount Holyoke College for permission to quote from *Willow Pollen, Little Miss Hilly;* (John Lane and Co., *The Four Seas,* Pub.); to Prof. Ada Snell for permission to use Irene Glascock's poems, *Adolescence,* and *Songs of Boredom;* to Wm. Wood & Co., Philadelphia for permission to use Fig. 53 and Fig. 90 from Cunningham's Anatomy; to Longmans, Green & Co. for permission to use copies of Fig. 79, P. 85 and drawings from Pp. 74 and 69 in Lickley's Physiology of the Nervous System; to the Saalfield Publishing Co., Akron, Ohio for use of their version of Mother Goose Rhymes; to the Judson Press, Philadelphia, and to W. L. Sly personally, for permission to quote from his book *World Stories Retold, the Boy and the Nuts, The Crow and the Pitcher, The Dog in the Manger, The*

*Shepard Boy and the Wolf; The Persian and his Sons, Why
the Bear Has a Stumpy Tail;* to Alfred Stokes & Co. for permission to quote from Alfred Noyes' *The Elfin Artist;* to
Vlynn Johnson for her poem *Friends;* to Anna Hempstead
Branch for use of her poems *Songs for my Mother;* to Richard
C. Burton for use of the poem *Across the Fields to Anne;* to
the Josephine Preston Peabody heirs for use of the poem
The House and the Road; to Richard Haven Schauffler for
use of a portion of the poem *Scum o' the Earth;* to Willa
Cather for use of the poem *Grandmither, Think Not I Forget;* to Bliss Carmen for use of *A Vagabond Song;* to T. B.
Aldrich for use of poem *An Old Castle;* to the Expression
Company for use of various poems for the publication of which
they hold the rights; to George Jacobs & Co., Philadelphia
for poem *All 'Round Our House;* Holland; to W. M. Letts
for use of poem *My Kerry Cow;* to Norreys Jephries O'Connor, personally for use of poems *Over the Dunes,* and *Queenstown Harbor,* from *Beside the Blackwater* by John Lane Co.,
N. Y., Publishers; to the Public School Pub. Co., for quotations from the Horn-Packer list of 5000 Commonest Words
in the Spoken Vocabulary of Children, from 24th Year Book,
1925; to Teacher's College Record for 1921, for words quoted
from the Thorndike list of 2500 Words in Common Use in
the Early Grades; to A. Rejall of the New York State Re-
gents', for quoting in full the First 1000 Words, which appeared in Supplement to Interstate Bulletin, Adult Elementary
Education, Apr.-May, 1925, Vol. 1, No. 2, by A. Rejall.

FOREWORD

This book deals with psychology in special relation to Speech, a subject to which Dr. Stinchfield has devoted herself throughout her teaching experience.

We feel a special interest in this book because of the author's former connection with the Pittsburgh Public Schools. Her first experience in our schools was in the dramatization department of McKelvy School. Her interest in speech was such that she was transferred from McKelvy School to the Department of Special Education. In this department Dr. Stinchfield did outstanding work with foreigners and children needing corrective work in speech.

While connected with the Pittsburgh Public Schools the author was awarded a Frick Scholarship to do special work in Columbia University.

After her graduation from the University of Pittsburgh, Dr. Stinchfield left the Pittsburgh Schools to join the staff of Dr. Seashore, University of Iowa. She was awarded her M.A. from this institution and her Ph.D. from the University of Wisconsin.

Dr. Stinchfield has continued her teaching and clinical activities at Mt. Holyoke College and Pennsylvania State College. Her work has been in a field that is highly important in all levels of school life — from the kindergarten through the college — and for this reason we recommend this book to all teachers interested in speech.

WILLIAM M. DAVIDSON,
Superintendent of Schools.

Pittsburgh, Pa.
October 4, 1928.

PREFACE

Interest in speech handicaps and personality difficulties related to the same are not new. In the early part of this century speech clinics and special classes for children with speech defects were organized in many cities in Europe. A little later such work was undertaken in this country in such centers as New Haven and New York, under Dr. Scripture, in Philadelphia under Dr. Witmer, and at the Polyclinic hospital, Philadelphia, under Dr. Mackuen; in Wisconsin under Dr. Blanton; in California by Dr. Stivers and by Mrs. Mabel Gifford, in Chicago by Dr. E. L. Kenyon. Speech-training for the deaf child was improved in method by the contributions of Miss Yale of the Clark School at Northampton, by Miss Bruhn's translation of the Müller-Waller Method of teaching the deaf, and by the work of the Central Institute for the Deaf in St. Louis. More recently speech correction work has been established in a large number of cities in connection with the public schools, and already a large number of teachers are employed exclusively for speech correction work in such cities as New York, Philadelphia, Boston, Jersey City, Buffalo, Harrisburgh, Pittsburgh, Chicago, Madison, St. Louis, Detroit, Grand Rapids, Des Moines, Cleveland, and further west in San Francisco and Los Angeles. These are only a few of the centers in which such work has been organized and conducted on a rather extensive scale, often with clinical facilities, medical advice and psychological service available for the speech teacher.

School authorities are realizing as never before that

not only should the schools offer means for overcoming such handicaps as deafness, poor vision and personality difficulties of the type so often found in handicapped children, but also that they must find a place in the school curriculum for the special training of the child who has a speech handicap which might prove to be both an economic and a social handicap in later life, in addition to retarding his progress in school. Such defects should be treated during the early formative years, and before the speech and voice reactions have become "set" and habitual, as a part of the child's total personality reaction.

The writer offers these exercises, not with any idea of covering the vast field of speech disorders which have already been extensively treated elsewhere,— nor with any idea of furnishing a complete bibliography of the types of speech defects treated in various medical texts on the subject. She wishes rather to offer, as a result of her own experience, a few practical suggestions and exercises which may be useful to the busy teacher of speech, who may be seeking special methods for a particular type of speech defect such as cleft-palate speech, deafness associated with a speech defect, stuttering and lisping which are found so frequently in the schools in urban communities. We realize that offering exercises is often a dangerous device, as no one exercise is infallible with any particular child, nor is any one "system" invariably successful in dealing with the speech defective. Moreover, the fact must always be borne in mind that each child should be treated as an *individual,* and that only as the teacher *understands her problem,* can she understand *which* exercises and *which* methods may best be *applied to the individual case.*

For suggestions made in the preparation of the manuscript, and for the reading of special chapters in this book, the writer wishes to express her indebtedness to Dr. and Mrs. S. P. Hayes of Mount Holyoke College, to Dr. Walter F. Dearborn of Harvard Graduate School of Education, to Dr. William Healy of the Judge Baker Foundation, Boston, to Supt. E. E. Allen of the Perkins Inst. for the Blind, Boston, and to Dr. O. H. Burritt of the Pennsylvania School for the Blind, to Principal Jane E. MacKenzie of the Pittsburgh Public Schools for reading and suggestions in regard to graded exercises used in the Supplement and elsewhere, to Sina V. Fladeland in charge of Corrective Speech work at Perkins Institution, Boston, for trying out these exercises with children in various grades; to the Editorial Staff of the Expression Company for suggestions and courtesies extended during the work of preparing this manuscript.

SARA M. STINCHFIELD.

South Hadley, Mass., August, 1928.

CONTENTS

Speech Pathology
with
Methods in Speech Correction

Part I

Chapter I

SPEECH DEFECTS AS A SPECIAL HANDICAP

*Special Handicaps in Reading and Writing.
Inequalities in Growth.*

EDUCATORS have pointed out that in the training of the child in the years from eight to twelve, certain types of skill, important to adult life, have their golden hour. If training is neglected in this period, when plasticity and ease of adjustment make it possible for a child to acquire new modes of reaction readily, the boy or girl will be at a disadvantage or under a heavy handicap in the struggle for success, later on. G. Stanley Hall refers to the 8-12 year period as the most favorable time for acquiring skill in reading, writing, drawing, manual training, musical technique, foreign language, pronunciation, and mathematics. He has pointed out the great changes which occur at adolescence, when attention shifts from the development of the fundamental muscles to the accessory muscles. During the earlier growth period activity centers in the larger muscle movements of the trunk, arms, legs, large joints, neck, back, hips, shoulders, knees, and elbows. People at a relatively low level of culture and with formal training may be highly skilled in performances involving the fundamental muscles yet remain unskilled in the development of the skilled movements of the accessory muscles of the hand, tongue, face and articulatory organs, as in writing, reading, talking, piano-playing and the like, which are on a higher plane. These movements are linked with psychical activity, and to the over-stressing of the finer coördinations involved in these performances have been traced some of the nervous reactions found in chorea, and nervous disturbances of various types. (18) Precocious development on the psychic side may produce excessive nervousness and muscular irritability on the physical side.

Establishment of Control.

THE value of using the fundamental muscles as a corrective agent in nervous diseases is well known. Its therapeutic value consists in the toning down of irritability, "fidgety" reactions, nervous tension and strain, by producing a return to "normalcy" in poise, self-control and psycho-physical balance. Characteristic motor movements may persist in children in their manner of expression, inflection, way of walking and talking; they may become exaggerated and persist in morbid forms such as stuttering, lisping, peculiarity of gait, handwriting, facial grimaces, and the like. Instead of gradually disappearing, they often remain among blind children, uncorrected by the use of the mirror, or "facial consciousness"; in the deaf they may persist as peculiar noises associated with speech; if uncorrected they may cause personality disturbances and unsocial attitudes on the part of the subject.

In studying a large number of children in two schools for the blind we have been surprised at the prevalence of speech defects among these children, not so much the severer forms known to the speech clinics in large centers, as the more ineffectual, inactive forms of articulation commonly called "oral inactivity", lisping, slovenly speech and stuttering. The handicap of blindness, of necessity puts a high premium upon training in mental functions, in order that the blind adult may be able to perform some useful work and attain some degree of independence in mental fields, since he cannot compete successfully in a large number of physical activities open to the seeing person. The diminution of physical activity and concentration upon the mental tends to render the blind child both more passive and more nervous than the seeing child. The muscles of expression eventually assume a certain passivity and lack of the play of expression and animation which one finds among seeing children. Dramatics, plays, games, cultivation of a sense of humor and the like might serve as correctives, but no amount of training in a purely mental sphere will arouse the play of expression and efforts at self-expression which come from motor activities. This need is being recognized more and more in the training of blind, deaf and deficient children, and provided for by the establishment of physical education classes, social dancing, games, dramatics and the like.

Reading and Writing.

THESE two are closely related functions, as both are expressional activities of man. Just as speech-understanding precedes active speech in infancy, so also the ability to read usually precedes the ability to write, because the visual adjustments required in reading are ready to function earlier than the finer accessory muscles involved in writing. Modern systems of reading require a child to read meanings into words as he pronounces them, or writes them. The "flash card" system

of learning to read has thus replaced the old alphabetic method of reading syllable by syllable. The technique used for securing skill and speed in oral and
silent reading has reached a rather dangerous stage,
in that we are finding a large number of children who
cannot progress at the rapid rate expected of the average child. Some children do not learn to read during
the entire first year in school. Upon being given tests
for intelligence we often find such children not only
up to the average in general knowledge and information, in form board tests and motor performances, but
we sometimes find that these children have unusual
talent in a certain direction such as in art or music.

Speed in learning to write is not expected to keep
pace with learning to read, but both writing and reading are more easily taught when related to oral expression. Investigations in the Boston Schools, made by
Dearborn and others (12) and in Iowa,* by Orton,
have revealed that certain children are unable to form
the necessary associations between the printed symbols or names of objects, the written form, and the
object visualized; they are often unable to learn to
read by modern methods, and must be taught by the
old, alphabetic method, memorizing and identifying
the individual letters, sounding the word-parts syllable
by syllable, and studying lists of similar words, until
they can be trained to observe for themselves slight
differences between word forms, sequence of letters,
word sounds, and the written symbols.

Dearborn (12) and others have found that children
may suffer from disability in reading (called "congeni-

*S. T. Orton. Training the Left Handed. Hygeia: 5, Sept. 1927, Pp.
451-454.
    Ibid. Studies in Stuttering. Arch. Neurol. & Psychiatry; Nov. 1927,
Pp. 671-672.

tal word-blindness") and yet recognize and read figures easily and correctly. The fact that figures present no difficulty rather indicates that the difficulty is psychical, not a physiological difficulty of vision. Dearborn further found that even when difficulty with both letters and numerals was encountered, the child was often able to learn to draw, write, copy or to recognize pictures. This further indicates that the difficulty is not a defect of vision.

First grade children, and even pre-school children, sometimes appear to be reading when they have memorized the words on a given page from hearing the pages read aloud, so that they are able to reproduce the entire page verbatim. Teachers have been deceived into believing that they have conquered the reading disability in certain children, because the child appeared to read entire pages from the reader, when as a matter of fact the child was repeating the contents of the book from memory, prompted by the pictures.

Dearborn and Lord found that the non-readers were weak in auditory memory span for numbers and letters. Even if the auditory memory span appears normal, it is often true that the visual memory span is weak, for the manner of speech development in the child has strengthened the auditory and glosso-kinaesthetic memories, at the expense of the visual memories.

Studies made by Dearborn (12) at the Harvard Graduate School of Education (12) indicate that there is a relationship between special disability in reading and the phenomenon of mirror-writing. "Mirror-writing" is usually associated with left-handedness. Consequently, the left-handed child showing peculiarities in the motor writing mechanism is especially liable to exhibit difficulties in learning to read. Quite frequently speech defects have also been found in these children. Psychologists now generally hold that there is not necessarily a congenital or hereditary defect in children of the non-reader type, but that inhibiting habits, weak auditory or visual memories, inadequate associations or linkage between the visual, auditory and motor speech centers are at the basis of the disability in reading. Feelings of inferiority are frequently found in these cases. Usually, however, there seems to be some type of intellectual shortcoming which specially handicaps or conditions the child's reactions. The left-handed child in writing must move his hand across the page from left to right, when his tendency is to move it from right to left. The right-handed person would feel very awkward if forced to write "in reverse", forming the letters from right to left of the page, and yet this is what we expect of the left-handed child. Because of this the left-handed child also makes errors in reading, as the eye-motor impulse is to read from right to left, when the word is written from left to right, so he reads "saw" as "was". Similar confusion is made on certain consonants of similar formation such as p and g; d and b; m and w. Many workers in the field of speech defects have reported a high percentage of stuttering among originally left-handed children who have been taught to use the right hand. This indicates that there is some "complication" or difficulty encountered in the speech-learning process. Dearborn (12) found that in cases where the auditory span was shorter than average, it was difficult to keep in mind the necessary sequence of phonetic elements. He often found his subjects lacking in pitch discrimination, and having speech defects, so that perception and memory of sounds heard and the kinaesthetic sensations connected with speech were inaccurate. In such cases he discovered that the ordinary methods of school drill were useless. Even though these defects are not serious enough to prevent a child from eventually learning to read and write, they are serious handicaps which require special training, individual attention, and special methods for their removal.

Dr. James Hinshelwood in 1917 found 31 non-reader cases, boys exceeding girls in number. His conclusions were that these children must have individual instruction, alone, with short and carefully graduated series of reading lessons daily; that visual memories must be educated by frequent repetition until they were "set" in memory. He found the old-fashioned method (alphabet learning, plus spelling of words) was superior to the "flash-card" or rapid-fire word exposure method of the modern school room.

Miss Lord in the Harvard Graduate School, (12) in training a child by special methods to overcome difficulties in reading, began by teaching words so that they could be recognized as idiograms, thence leading to the ability to read unfamiliar words. She tried out various pedagogical methods, combining visual, auditory and kinaesthetic sensations. About two months was given to improving auditory span for words heard and spelled. Five-letter words were spelled correctly at the end of this time, but there was much difficulty with words of over five letters. Writing was employed to improve kinaesthetic sensation and word perception, but ability to *write* the word did not improve the ability to *spell* it, she found. Words drawn or printed for the subject did not help. The subject often confused similar words such as "look" and "like". The experimenter then adopted the plan of printing difficult parts of the word in red ink, and after several days of drill on the words, recognized by the red letters in some, the subject was able to distinguish them more easily when all the word was printed in black. For training, she selected the story of Peter Rabbit, in pictorial edition, typing a special version, so as to eliminate the difficult words. By the time the story was completed, phonetic drill had enabled the child to read correctly by means of phonetic analysis and synthesis. About fifteen minutes a day was given to this drill. There seemed to be no transfer of training, however. Spelling the word did not seem to aid in learning to write it. The process of building up auditory, visual, motor-speech and motor-writing bonds or connections in the association areas of the brain was found to be more difficult than in the case of the average child.

We have found that much the same conditions exist in many children and adolescents having speech disorders such as lisping, oral inaccuracies or indistinct speech. That is, pitch discrimination is poor, auditory memory span is weak, and special individual training is necessary to strengthen the auditory memories for sounds, to build up the glosso-kinaesthetic sensations, and to seek to develop the connections between the visual-auditory and motor speech and writing centers. "The last stage in the reading process is the acquirement and storage of the visual memories of words", says Hinshelwood. If the visual or auditory memories for words are weak, part of the word may be inaccurately reproduced, in speech or writing, and with each faulty repetition, the inaccurate form tends to become more firmly set and more difficult to break up. This is as true of habits formed by the stutterer as by the non-reader or poor speller. The stutterer though often an omnivorous reader, is notoriously faulty in recognition and repetition of difficult words, or words of several syllables. The stutterer often stumbles over long words, or mispronounces, even when he does not stutter over them. He seems to be lacking in auditory imagery for difficult linguistic performances, even though he reads much without digesting or attempting to pronounce or even to understand the material he reads. His stuttering thus may sometimes be a defense mechanism to protect him from the difficulties of reading hard or uninteresting material.

Gates (16) and Schmitt (30) in studying disabilities in reading find not only nothing pathological, but nothing congenital at the basis of the difficulty. The same may be said of the phenomena of stuttering, and certain other types of speech disturbances. Many writers have confused *defects* with *special disabilities* in reading and spelling. We must remember that in the case of *defective* intelligence, little can be done to remedy the difficulty in spelling and reading. Yet even here the case is not hopeless. Much has been accomplished with seemingly hopeless material in the special opportunity classes in the public schools, where reading, writing, spelling, and speech difficulties are frequent. In the case of a special disability in learning to read, write or spell, individual drill, special attention and learning by slower methods give appreciable results. The learning process must involve the setting of memories of the auditory, visual and glosso-kinaesthetic types.

Miss Hincks (19) found in her work at the Harvard Laboratory that the non-reader children exhibited great difficulty in recognizing differences in sounds. It has been found to be true of a large number of college women, held for speech correction during the years 1922-27 at Mount Holyoke College, that auditory imagery seemed to be very poor, pitch discrimination below average, and that the ability to detect differences in sounds play a large part in their special handicap (ineffective, inaccurate speech of the oral inaccuracy type).

Psychologists find the correlation between reading difficulty and defective pitch hard to explain. If consonants be regarded as atonic or "noises", as described by Borden and Busse (7) while vowels may be described as "tones", it may be that experimenters will find that the difficulty of the non-reader and some speech defectives with phonetic vowel sounds is due to defective power of pitch discrimination. It has been found by Kohler and Jaensch in Germany that vowel sounds u, o, a, e and i are ascending tones approximately an octave apart. Bezold represents vowel E as extending from about A¹ to Aᵐ, while vowel I is pitched close to Aᵐ.* It is possible that tonal gaps or "islands of deafness" for certain parts of the musical scale, together with poor auditory discrimination may be responsible for difficulty in learning to read, to pronounce clearly, to spell, and to recognize sounds in a given language.

In conclusion we wish to summarize certain findings of Miss Hincks, as there is a close correlation between the neuropathic background which she finds in the non-reader child, and that which various investigators have found in the histories of stutterers, neurotic lispers, "clutterers", and other types of rapid, over-reacting, ineffective speakers.

*Bezold. Das Horvermogen der Taubstummen. Bergman, Wiesbaden. 1896. Tafel 9.

Miss Hincks finds that reading difficulty has a hereditary basis, and is found in neuropathic stock. (19) McCready (23) also found that many cases of the non-reader type were from families where also were found alcoholism, insanity, hysteria, stammering, "nervousness" and epileptic convulsions. Miss Hincks found that in most of the case-histories nervous traits were exhibited, either in the child itself or in the immediate family. Her subjects showed such reactions as nightmares, hesitation in speech, anxiety about health, willfulness, rudeness to elders, stubbornness, untruthfulness, oversensitiveness, boastfulness, selfishness, repression, high fatigability and emotional outbreaks of crying and tantrums. Certain irregularities such as difficulties in reading were found to be transmissible in stock which is highly organized and nervously unstable, and where there is not usually the *patience and persistence* to overcome them. When these are found in families of intellectual achievement, there is an added stigma and distress in the mind of the child which aggravates the difficulty. This develops an unfortunate state of tension, general nervousness in the child, irritation of parents, and a general family and school maladjustment occurs. It was found that mental handicaps such as difficulty in learning to read, write and spell have serious effects upon the character development and personality of the child.

In the case of speech disturbances with a neuropathic background, it is not the speech habit itself and the lack of tone standards or clear enunciation which are especially to be deplored, unfortunate as these may be. It is rather the flabbiness of will, the undesirable character traits, avoidance-reactions and lack of moral stamina and determination which speech defects seem to engender, and which seem to bring about a "vicious circle" of reactions more closely allied to speech, personality and social adjustment than we have hitherto realized. (41)

Practise in oral reading in the early grades helps a child to build up associations between actual experiences, and the written or printed symbols related to the same. In the later grades and during adolescence, the child begins to realize the social and recreational value of language. As many children may never read poetry and verse after the eighth grade, it should at least be introduced to them in this period. Stone holds that 60 to 80 percent of the time devoted to reading in the lower grades should be given to oral work, while the time intervening between the early and later grades may be more profitably devoted to silent reading and training for speed in reading and comprehension. The report of the National Committee on Reading (1925) recommends that pupils be taught to read both orally and silently from the very beginning devoting *equal amounts of time to both in the first grade.* This report also recommends that in connection with oral training of first grades the children should be taught to express themselves in regard to a wide range of interests: should be trained in a reasonable facility in use of ideas; should gain sufficient command of simple English to speak with ease and freedom; should acquire a relatively wide vocabulary, with accuracy in enunciation and pronunciation; should develop a genuine desire to read. It was also recommended that "no separate work in phonetics should be done until the child has established the habit of thought-getting, has a reasonable stock of words, and has begun to notice gross similarities and differences."

Experience in various localities points out certain dangers in the use of some types of phonic systems in the first grade, except as employed incidentally for correcting errors of pronunciation, articulation, language difficulties, and confusion between voiced and voiceless consonants in a given language. Over emphasis, has in some localities been blamed for the onset of stuttering, as the monotonous repetition of a consonant such as "m-m-m", or "d-d-d", may, in the case of a nervous or suggestible child, inculcate faulty habits of speech.

Stone gives as one of the general objectives of reading, the development of the ability to convey meaning and feeling to another person. He believes that this may be done through the effective teaching of poems, and through their oral rendition. He calls attention to the great difference in speed in reading, between the first and later grades. Thus in the primary grades the child's interpretation of the meaning of a given passage rarely runs ahead of the rate of vocalization, but by the time he finishes the third grade his rate in comprehension of meaning far exceeds his rate of articulation in oral reading; by the time he reaches the seventh grade he can recognize words twice as fast as he can pronounce them. This leads to the conclusion that too great emphasis upon phonics and oral reading, without attention to rapid recognition of words or phrases may retard the development of an effective silent reading rate. Stone therefore holds that it is dangerous to over-stress oral reading beyond the third grade, at least until the later grades are reached.

We believe however that there are certain dangers in the present emphasis upon silent reading and the speeding-up processes of present day methods. Not only are the reticent, timid child and the slow reader

liable to continue to be over-timid, and slow in oral
reading, but they may be unable to compete successfully in many performances which might be open to
them if they involved less silent reading ability, and
more oral expression of ideas. It has been found by
Piaget* and others that the child's early expressions
in the kindergarten and early grades are largely ego-
centric, and are what he calls the "unsocial mono-
logue"; that is the child talks for the pleasure and
satisfaction of doing so. Much of the time he has no
idea of getting an answer. The more active, alert
and intelligent the child, the more he talks. His thinking deals with concrete objects, rather than with ab-
stract images. With adults, often the reverse is true,
the *more* they think, the *less* they talk, and during their
most productive periods in a given field they may not
express themselves in overt speech at all, while silent
speech is very active. (37) The adult deals with ab-
stract images rather than with the concrete, much of
the time. We know that there are dangers, for the
adult in too prolonged seclusion and too little opportunity for self-expression. Gregariousness and sympathy cause man to share his thoughts with others, to
respond to social behavior in others, to assume ag-
gressive attitudes, and to defend or to protect others
through speech as well as through other forms of behavior.

The old reading books have long since been displaced by many series of graded stories, but we find
in few of the modern series any such directions as
those to be found in the old Monroe's Sixth Readers
of the edition of 1872. Here are 43 pages devoted to
rules and directions and explanations for effective

*Piaget. The Language and Thought of the Child.

reading of the selections given. The directions called attention to posture, breathing, thought and feeling, making one's self heard and understood, and to how to study the selection. Vocal analysis includes notes on quality, articulation, volume of tone, inflection, rate of utterance, pitch, transition, and style, *with appropriate passages from literature to illustrate each.*

Other readers, (24) dating back as far as 1825 divide selections up into groups such as narrative, didactic, argumentative, and pathetic "pieces", dialogues, public speeches (orations) and "promiscuous" selections. In one such reader eighteen pages in the introduction are devoted to the question of vocal interpretation, under the heads of loudness, distinctness, rate, pronunciation, emphasis, tone, pauses and manner of reading.

The Village Reader in use in 1844 condenses much of the reading directions to a page called Hints for Teachers. (36) In addition to an explanation of various punctuation marks, one finds nine rules for oral reading which include attention to pitch, pronunciation, pauses, breath control, rate, emphasis, and inflection. A page is devoted to "common errors" such as tendencies to clip word endings, to mutilate certain vowel or consonant sounds, to mispronounce and to use provincial forms.

The emotional appeal made by the old "Lyceum" program, and the contacts gained with various authors, through the readers is evident from the keen enjoyment and relish with which people of a former day and generation repeat to their children those poems and ballads committed to memory for many a Lyceum entertainment. In our factual learning and emphasis upon "skimming" it is possible that we are los-ing a valuable form of memory training, as well as certain mental and moral values instilled by the poetry of other days. Hamlin Garland (15) writes of those days as follows:—

"On Fridays we generally attended the Lyceum, which met in the Burr-Oak School House. We often debated, and on one occasion I attained to the honor of being called upon to preside. Another memorable evening is that in which I read with what seemed to me distinguished success Joaquin' Miller's magnificent new poem *Kit Carson's Ride* and in the splendid roar and trample of its lines discovered a new and powerful American poet. I read every line of his, which the newspapers or magazines brought to me and was profoundly influenced by its epic quality.

"I wish to acknowledge my deep obligation to Prof. McGuffey, for the dignity and grace of his selections in our readers. From these pages we learned to know and love the poems of Scott, Byron, Southey, Wordsworth and a long line of the English masters. I had my first taste of Shakespeare from the selected scenes in these books. With terror as well as delight I rose to read Lochiel's Warning, The Battle of Waterloo, or The Roman Captive; Marco Bozzaris and William Tell were alike glorious to me.

"We were taught to feel the force of these poems and to reverence the genius that produced them, and that was worth while. Falstaff and Prince Hal, Henry and his wooing of Kate, Wolsey and his downfall, Shylock and his pound of flesh all *became a part of our thinking* and helped us to measure the larger figures of our own literature.

"Never again shall I feel the same exultation, the same pleasure mingled with sadness, the same perception of the irrevocable passing of beautiful things and the equally irrevocable coming on of care and trouble, as filled my heart on graduation day. I had taken 'Going West' as the subject for my oration. . . . . . and upon it I had lavished a great deal of anxious care. Feeling dimly but sincerely the epic march of the American Pioneer I had tried to express it in my address. I should not like to have that manuscript printed precisely as it came from my pen, and a phonographic record of my voice would serve admirably as an instrument of blackmail. However, I thought at the time that I had done well, and my mother's shy smile confirmed me in the belief."

Reading and Language Ability.

WE have devoted considerable space to the consideration of the psychology of language, its physical and mental bases. We know that the study of language covers a wide field, including not only the art of communication through articulate speech, but also such related fields as spelling, writing, reading, grammar, literature, both oral and written composition. Reading involves perception, visual and auditory memories, interpretation of oral and written symbols, comprehension, motor reactions, emotions, and complex learning processes. Linguistic ability has been shown to increase with age and grade. Trabue's tests show that sex influences language ability to some extent, as he finds that girls usually obtain higher grades in English in school, than do boys. Even in written composition the girls excelled the boys, on Trabue's language scales.* He found the average length of sentence in

*Trabue. Norms for Language Scales in Relation to Grade and Age. Teachers College, Columbia University, N. Y.

twelve-year-old high school girls to be 18.4 words, while that of the boy was 14.9 words. Girls of twelve were found to be about a year ahead of boys of the same age in their composition work. That there is a correlation between language ability and intelligence seems evident from the findings of Trabue and others. Trabue found a coefficient of correlation of +.83 between his language scales and the mental age, in the Binet Tests.

Charters in his study of errors in language, (26) in the Pittsburgh Schools, (1919) found that the 25,676 errors collected from oral language of school pupils fell into five main classes, which made up 71% of the total errors. These are given in the following table:

Principal classes of errors in Spoken English.

Wrong verb (*lie* for *lay,* etc.) 18%
Syntactical redundance (this here, etc.) 16%
Confusion of past tense and perfect participle
    (*seen* for *saw,* etc.) 14%
Failure of verb to agree with subject in person
    and number (he don't. etc.) 13%
Double negative (not-no, etc.) 10%

                                —
Total of the five classes 71%

Brown, of Cockery School, Chicago, (26) has made an interesting attempt to locate these errors by grades, in order that by location teachers may better be able to apply effective drill, and remove as early as possible these mistakes in language.

Reed, in writing of the Psychology of Language says (26) "there are almost no school children who can give a clear, coherent, and errorless oral discourse without special training; the schools must therefore offer a good deal of work in correct speaking in order to make this possible. It will help not only in oral speech but in written, as has been shown by experiment in the high schools of Illinois."

References.

1. ALLPORT. *Social Psychology.* Houghton Mifflin Co., Boston, 1924, pp. 169-198.
2. BALLARD, P. B. *Sinistrality and Speech.* Journal Exp. Ped. 1911-12.
3. BIRMINGHAM-KRAPP. *First Lessons in Speech Improvement.* Scribners, 1922.
4. BISCH. *Clinical Psychology.* Williams & Wilkins, Baltimore, 1925.
5. BLANTON. *Child Guidance.* Century Co., New York, 1926, pp. 94-110: 288-294.
6. BLANTON-STINCHFIELD. *Speech Measurements.* C. H. Stoelting Co., Chicago.
7. BORDEN-BUSSE. *Speech Correction.* F. C. Crofts Co., N. Y., 1925, p. 47.
8. BURNHAM. *The Normal Mind.* D. Appleton & Co., N. Y., 1924, p. 320; p. 435.
9. BURT, CYRIL. *Mental and Scholastic Tests.* 1921, P. S. King Co., P. 286.
10. CONRADI, E. *Psychol. and Pathol. of Speech Development.* Ped. Sem. 11, 1904, pp. 328-380.
11. DEARBORN, W. F. *The Psychology of Reading.* Archiv. of Philos. Psychol. and Scientific Method, March, 1906, Chapter 3.
12. DEARBORN, LORD AND CARMICHAEL. *Special Disabilities in Learning to Read and Write.* Harvard Monog. in Education, June, 1925. Harvard Univ. Press, Cambridge, Massachusetts.
13. DOWNEY. *The Will Temperament and Its Testing.* World Book Co., 1923, pp. 229-243.
14. FREEMAN. *The Psychology of the Common Branches.* Houghton Mifflin Co., 1916.
15. GARLAND, HAMLIN. *A Son of the Middle Border.* Macmillan Co., 1917.
16. GATES, A. I. *The Psychology of Reading and Spelling with Special Reference to Disability.* Teachers College Contrib. to Educa. No. 129, 1922.
17. GRAY. *Oral and Silent Reading.* Houghton Mifflin Co., 1926.
18. HALL, G. STANLEY. *Youth, Its Education and Regime.* D. Appleton Co., N. Y., 1907.
19. HINCKS, ELIZ. M. *Disability in Reading and Its Relation to Personality.* Harvard Monog. in Education, Harvard University Press, 1926.
20. HINSHELWOOD, J. *Word-Letter-Mind-Blindness.* London, 1900.
21. HOLLINGWORTH, L. *Special Talents and Defects.* Macmillan Co., 1923, pp. 69-96.
22. HUEY, E. B. *The Psychology and Pedagogy of Reading.* Macmillan, 1913.
23. McCREADY, E. B. *The Relation of Stuttering to Amusia.* Journ. A. M. A., July, 1910.
    IBID. *Congenial Word Blindness as a Cause of Backwardness in School Children.* Penn. Med. Journal, January, 1910.

24. MURRAY, LINDLAY. *The English Reader.* T. Bedlington, Boston, 1825.
25. PARSONS. *Left-handedness.* Macmillan Co., N. Y., 1924.
26. REED. *The Psychology of Elementary School Subjects.* Ginn & Co., 1927, pp. 273-283.
27. ROBBINS. *Stammering.* Boston Stammerers Inst. 1926, p. 121.
28. SCRIPTURE. *Stuttering and Lisping.* Macmillan, 1914, p. 251.
29. SCRIPTURE-JACKSON. *Manual for the Correction of Speech Disorders.* F. A. Davis Co., Phila., 1925.
30. SCHMITT, CLARA. *Developmental Alexia.* Elem. Sch. Jour. Vol. 18, 1918.
31. STINCHFIELD, S. M. *The Formulation and Standardization of a Series of Graded Speech Tests.* Psychol. Mono. Series, 1923. Vol. 33, No. 2.
32. STONE. *Oral and Silent Reading.* Houghton Mifflin Co., 1926.
33. TERMAN. *The Hygiene of the School Child.* Houghton Mifflin Co., Boston, 1914, pp. 335-360.
34. TRABUE. *Measure Your Mind.* Doubleday Page & Co., 1920.
35. TREDGOLD. *Mental Deficiency.* P. 132. (Consonantal defects.)
36. *Village Reader.* Merriam Co., Springfield, 1844.
37. WATSON. *Psychology from the Standpoint of the Behaviorist.* Lippincott, Phila., 1919, Pp. 310-347.
38. WEST, R. *Purposive Speaking.* Macmillan Co., 1924.
39. WEST, R. *Diagnosis of Speech Defects.* Wisconsin, 1926.
40. WHITE, W. *Outline of Psychiatry.* Nerv. & Ment. Dis. Pub. Co., Washington, D. C., 1921, 8th edition. 355 p.
41. WILLIAMS, T. *Dreads and Besetting Fears.* Little Brown Co., Boston, 1923, Pp. 39-50.
42. WOOLLEY AND FERRIS. *Diagnosis and Treatment of Young School Failures.* Gvt. Print. Office Bulletin No. 1. Washington, 1923. Bur. of Edu. Department of Interior.

Chapter II

A WORKING CLASSIFICATION WITH COMMON TERMINOLOGY

Speech Defects Classified.

AN attempt to classify speech defects under satisfactory headings leads to somewhat arbitrary groupings, if they are to be useful and practical. We should include practically all known types of speech disorders discussed in the current literature on the subject. Terms applied to speech disturbances cover a wide range. Medical men use terms which are often incomprehensible to the layman. The psychologist proposes other terms which seem to be explanatory from his standpoint. The teacher and the layman use simpler terms which may mean the same thing as the technical language applied by their professional confrères. Blanton (3) gives four types of stuttering, for instance. He speaks of the stutterer of the hypomanic type, the hysterical stutterer, the anxious, nervous type, and the stutterer suffering from organic or functional disorders. Scripture (15) gives three types of lisping, the organic, negligent and neurotic. Swift (18) attributes stuttering to visual or auditory amnesia, of a transient type. Many specialists use the terms stuttering and stammering interchangeably, although by derivation they mean very different things; stuttering referring to difficult labored speech and stammering to mispronunciation. Hence stammering is applied by the Germans to all forms of lisping, letter substitution or oral inaccuracies of whatever type.

Coriat (4) considers stuttering an anxiety neurosis, and not merely a "tic" or spastic coördination neurosis. The articulation of explosive sounds is especially difficult for stutterers, as the utterance is blocked at the stop-points for vowels and consonants in the peripheral speech mechanism, although the cause of the blocking or inhibition has been found to lie within the central nervous system and the higher cortical centers. The respiratory, muscular and psychic processes are not coördinated and *there is often a simultaneous blocking of the respiratory, diaphragmatic and laryngeal muscles whenever the delay occurs.

In the examination of some 600 stutterers, Colombat is said to have found not a single case presenting a history of organic defects in the articulating organs themselves. Italians recognized the utility of the facial grimaces of stutterers, by giving them a place in certain comedies. (II Tartaglia).

Speech is an acquired reaction, which must be learned by each succeeding generation. Stuttering cannot therefore be "inherited." It seems probable, from the large number of cases studied by various authors, and the appearance of stuttering in successive generations that there may be an hereditary transmission of the disposition or type of nervous system which predisposes the patient to stuttering habits. Most writers agree that bad example in the home, faulty education and psychotic tendencies, are the common causes of stuttering.

In the treatment of stuttering the best results are attained when the case is considered as a psycho-physical problem, and when suggestion and mental and

*See Studies of Travis at Iowa State Univ. Univ. of Iowa Studies, 1926-28.

physical therapy are all employed to break up the undesirable speech habits and to replace them by socially
desirable ones.

The following working classification has been found
useful in teacher training and in the explanation of
various types of speech defects, to laymen, teachers
and parents. Practically all speech defects which are
encountered in the school room, in the home and in
institutions or are discussed in literature on the subject, may be placed appropriately under one of six
general headings.*

These are:—

A. Alalia;   Delayed Speech, or absence of speech since
                birth.
B. Dyslalia;   Oral Inaccuracy, including lisping, careless
                enunciation, indistinct utterance and letter
                substitutions or mutations.
C. Dysarthria; Stuttering (stammering).
D. Dysphonia;   Aphonia or loss of voice after it has been
                once acquired.
E. Aphasia;   Aphasia, partial or complete loss of speech.
F. Distonia;   Vocal Defects of Quality.

Alalia or Delayed Speech.

THIS term is applied to the absence of voice or speech
from birth and persisting into the period when speech
should normally appear. Most children have a vocabulary of many consonant and vowel sounds at the end
of the first year. Normally the first speech period begins between the age of a year and a year and six
months. When walking is delayed, the speech development is also usually late. Speech normally represents a

*Terminology recommended by Committee on Speech Classifica-
tions for The American Society for the Study of the Disorders of
Speech.

"convergence of external and internal factors" of growth. If the sensory stimuli are reduced by the absence or arrest of some sensory avenue, the child may suffer retardation in speech development. In delayed speech development therefore, one usually thinks first of deafness as the possible cause. If the hearing is intact, one may suspect that there is a mental defect which may be determined by the application of standardized intelligence tests. (19) If there is no defect in intelligence one suspects that there is some psychic disturbance or special defect which is responsible for the arrest of development in speech. It may be that the child was left-handed at birth and has been forced to change from left to right in motor performances, and that this has interfered with linguistic development as seems highly probable from investigations made by Dearborn (6) and others. Dearborn has found that disabilities in learning to read and write are closely related to the speech function. The large number of left-handed children having speech defects, and referred to by various authorities in the field of speech correction, from time to time, is evidence of the possible interference in motor coördination and in psychic function which may occur as the result of forcing a left-handed child to become right-handed.

DELAYED speech appears in current literature under the following titles:—

1. Alalia.
2. Aphemia.
3. Dumbness.
4. Lingual arrests of development.
5. Mutism.
6. Deaf-mutism.

7. Hearing mutism.
8. Hysterical mutism.
9. Lalophobia.
10. Phonophobia (fear of talking).

II. Dysalia or Oral Inaccuracy. (3)

ORAL inaccuracy is an ineffective manner of producing speech sounds. It does not refer to pronunciation or to emphasis, but to the lack of clearness or incisiveness in utterance.

Some part of the speech mechanism functions ineffectively. It may be the tongue, teeth, lips, hard palate or jaw. Within the boundaries covered by this definition we find such defects of speech as the following :—

1. Lalophobia.
2. Idioglossia.
3. Infantile speech.
4. Articulatory kinaesthesia.
5. Lethargic speech.
6. Lisping (frontal sigmacism; lateral sigmacism; simple sigmacism).
7. Lalling.
8. Mutations.
9. Dyslalia.
10. Negligent speech.
11. Slovenly speech.
12. Sluggish speech.
13. Stammering.
14. Foreign accent.
15. Letter substitution.
17. Indistinct speech.

Oral inaccuracy may accompany such organic conditions as hereditary ataxia, multiple sclerosis, tongue-tie, paralysis, bulbar palsy, meningitis, paresis or toxic conditions of other types. It is often called (1) anarthria (unintelligible speech); (2) bradylalia (slowness); (3) scamping (baby speech); (4) dysarthria; (5) ataxic speech.

Oral inaccuracies also occur as a result of developmental defects in the vocal mechanism as in the cleft-palate speech. They also occur under the head "nasality", "throaty" tones, etc. We find the following terms applied to oral inaccuracies of organic and functional origin.

18. Slurring speech.
    a. Of Organic origin.
    b. Of Functional origin.
19. Articulatory amnesia.
20. Mutilations.
21. Dislogia.
22. Phonetic defects.
23. Nasal sigmatism.
24. Nasal parasigmacism.
25. Paralambdacism: pararhotacism, etc.
26. Logorrhea.
27. "Nigger-boy" speech.

III. Dysarthria or Stuttering. (15)

WE have already presented a definition of stuttering. It is usually defined as a form of motor-incoördination or an anxiety neurosis in which the speech disturbance is a prominent symptom. The motor speech impulse is not coördinated with the motor speech musculature, and there is consequently a lag or delay in transmission. This occasions a blocking, inhibition, or cramp in some part of the peripheral speech mechanism. The speech is hesitant, there may be utter inability to articulate words or phrases, or there may be a tendency to repeat final words or sound units, causing jerky unrhythmic utterance. We find the following terms in current literature on the subject.

1. Stuttering.
2. Stammering.
3. Speech hesitation.
4. Speech blocking.
5. Speech stumbling.
6. Speech pressure.
7. Broken rhythm.
8. Hysterical stutter.
9. Choreatic stutter.
10. Balbus Blaesus.
11. Begaiement, (from the French).
12. Das Stottern, (from the German).
13. Tetanic stutter.
14. Phanerogenetic stuttering.
15. Cryptogenetic stuttering.

It has been estimated that one-half of one percent to one percent of school children stutter. The stuttering is a symptom,—not a disease. The fault is often in the home training, in diet, over-stimulation, nervousness and various forms of maladjustment. The majority of children are capable of making the finer coördinations necessary for the highly skilled speech movements of tongue, lips, soft-palate and jaw, in rhythm with respiratory, diaphragmatic and laryngeal mechanisms. This takes some years of experimentation and is a gradual learning process. One finds that some children seem unable to acquire these muscle coördinations easily and if there is unusual excitation or nervousness, they may stutter almost at the beginning of articulate speech.

Nervous instability and stuttering are closely re-

lated, and the speech is a symptom of the accompanying mental and physical maladjustment. Stuttering
children should be carefully supervised as to rest, diet,
exercise, recreation, habits of work and play, and
general hygiene of mind and body. The nervous child
often improves rapidly in a new environment. A temporary absence from home of older brothers or sisters who may be the disturbing elements in the home
often relieves the symptoms of the nervous child and
enables him to readapt to family life successfully. A
domineering parent or brother and sister unduly irri-
tate a duller child in many homes. Sometimes the child
needs to be taken from the home for a period, and
placed under supervision where whims and vagaries
may not be too easily indulged. Speech improvement in
the stutterer is inseparable from physical and mental
hygiene.

Disturbances of the intestinal tract, irritation of the
gums, an organ inferiority following some childhood
disease such as St. Vitus' Dance, muscle spasms, enure-
sis, somnambulism are all significant in the history of
the stutterer. The child may be either dull or precocious and may stutter as a result of over-excitation. The
speech may have bred an inferiority complex so that
the child is unsocial, brooding, melancholy, suspicious
and hypersensitive. He shows fear of social situations
and exhibits a tendency to avoid meeting difficulties
squarely. This often makes it difficult to deal with him
on the same basis as with other children. There seems
to be a weakness of will, a moral "flabbiness" which
has been induced or exaggerated by the speech condition. Although speech is not inherited and each
generation must acquire language for itself, there are
evidences that a congenital weakness of the speech

muscles or an organ inferiority is often present in stutterers. In the history of a number of stutterers examined one finds such physical factors as tetany in infancy, rickets, dietary disturbances, convulsions, and habit spasms. If a stutter or speech hesitation accompanies the speech-learning process it is very difficult to eradicate it in later years. Corrective treatment is most effective at the onset of the difficulty. Passing months or years increase the difficulty in forming new habits of speech, and in displacing undesirable ones.

After considerable training in adulthood, lapses often occur. When treatment is begun in childhood the cure is often permanent.

IV. Dysphonia; Aphonia. (17)

THIS is a loss of voice or phonation, due to psychic disturbances, to partial arrest of lingual development, or to impairment of the vocal chords. It may be temporary or permanent. In voluntary whispering we have an example of "aphonia". Congestion of the larynx during laryngitis is an example of loss of speech due to organic conditions. In severe cases of croup and whooping cough, it is possible that the larynx may become sufficiently congested to cause loss of phonation. Sometimes it has a functional rather than an organic basis, as in hysteria or other psychic disturbances. During the war it often accompanied paralysis, shellshock and partial asphyxiation. During the period of treatment it was found that suggestion played an important part in the speech therapy. An hereditary tendency to vocal difficulties seemed to increase the liability to this type of speech disorder. In character it is a whispered tone, or a hoarse, breathy tone in quality; in a severe form both phonation and whispered speech are lost. It appears in literature under these headings:—

1. Absence of voice in negatively suggestible children.
2. Absence of voice in fear neurosis.
3. Fear of speech (phonophobia).
4. Voluntary whispering.
5. Psych-motor retardation (as in the non-reader).
6. Voice amnesia.
7. Hysterical aphonia and aphemia.
8. Lack of phonation due to arrested development.
9. Partial arrest of lingual development.

V. Aphasia. (14)

MUCH has been written in medical literature on aphasia, which is the most dreaded of speech disorders and one which it is difficult to diagnose because of its possible complications. In aphasia there is a loss or impairment of the speech function, due to lesions in the motor, sensory or associational areas of the brain cortex. Cerebral lesions, traumatic neurosis, shock, toxic conditions and prolonged strain or worry seem to be the most frequent causes. It is found among the feeble-minded and the insane, and not uncommon in cases of nervous breakdown and exhaustion.

Southard (17) describes its frequent appearance during the World War of 1914-18 among "shell-shocked" soldiers. He found an interference with mnemonic functions, of short or long duration, among those suffering from traumatic neurosis or other forms of psychoneurosis. It varies from a temporary loss of memory and power of association, hysterical deafness and dumbness, to permanent derangement, but in most cases a few weeks or months in the hospi-

tal was sufficient to bring about complete restoration.
According to the location of the cerebral lesion, it is
referred to as cortical or subcortical, and of the sensory, motor or association type. When both sensory
and motor areas are affected, total aphasia results. It
may be a defect or an utter loss of function in such
activities as speech, reading, writing or sign language.

Some of the varieties most common in the literature of aphasia are:

1. Motor aphasia.
2. Sensory aphasia.
3. Agraphia; paragraphia.
4. Auditory aphasia.
5. Associational aphasia.
6. Transitory aphasia.
7. Visual verbal amnesia.
8. Word blindness.
9. Word deafness.
10. Alexia; paralexia.
11. Ataxic aphasis.
12. Apraxia.
13. Anarthria (motor).
14. Dysphasia.
15. Paraphasia.
16. Cortical and subcortical aphasia.
17. Transcortical sensory aphasia (with loss of comprehension of speech and writing).
18. Word dumbness.
19. Subcortical motor aphasia.
20. Cortical sensory aphasia.
21. Amnesic aphasia.
22. Broca's aphasia, (motor).
23. Conduction aphasia.
24. Gibberish aphasia.
25. Mixed aphasia (motor and sensory).

VI. Vocal Defects.*

VOCAL defects are chiefly those of pitch, strength and character or quality. Quality is timbre or kind of tone dependent upon the number and intensity of the upper partials accompanying the fundamental tone. Voices differ in richness, resonance, mellowness and are somewhat dependent upon the mental attitude of the speaker. A mind stirred by imagination and feeling tends to produce a livelier, more harmonious result than one of a more prosaic, unemotional turn. Constrictions of muscles controlling the action of the vocal cords, the mouth and nasal passages modify the quality of tone produced. An open, non-obstructed tone passage produces better vowel quality than a deformed, narrow and constricted resonance chamber.

Pitch refers to the position of a sound in the musical scale, dependent upon the rate of vibrations of the sounding body. The more rapid the vibration, the higher the pitch. Nervous, excitable people speak rapidly and thus raise the pitch of their voices well above the fundamental tone. After a time they may permanently alter the pitch of the speaking voice from habitual misuse.

Ordinarily with the onset of adolescence, the masculine voice changes in pitch and quality, as well as increases in volume. The feminine voice does not pass through such radical changes because of difference in physiological conditions. The girl reaches maturity at a slightly earlier period than the boy, yet her voice does not noticeably change, and she is therefore less liable to self-consciousness on account of vocal peculiarities at this period. Many boys begin to stutter at

*Dorsey-Stinchfield. A Preliminary Classification of Speech Defect Terminology. Oralism and Auralism. St. Louis, Mo., July, 1926.

the onset of puberty, especially those who are excessively nervous, irritable, constitutionally inferior or maladjusted. The effeminate, girlish voice is sometimes found in men. This cannot usually be effectively dealt with, as it is usually based upon glandular secretions and their relation to maturing functions, rather than upon speech habits. In the same way, the brusque, mannish voice in girls is sometimes found, possibly due to oversecretions of some of the ductless glands. It is difficult here, also to alter the fundamental quality of the voice. It is often possible to improve the quality of thin, high-pitched voices, by vocal drill and exercises. These cases present a more hopeful prognosis. Physiological maturity often brings about an improvement in the vocal register, and a speaking voice may lose its high soprano quality and become contralto. This may be aided by vocal exercises and voice culture.

Among the unpleasing qualities of voice we find the acute, shrill, coarse, raucous, dull, gloomy, melancholic, gutteral, harsh, nasal, husky, metallic, strident, "throaty" tones. Under pitch difficulties we find the high-pitched, infantile voice; also the monotonous, sharp, sombre, toneless, subdued and flat. Poor breath control and weak volume of tone gives a muffled, dead thick tone, or one which is faint and of poor carrying power. It may be breathy, aspirate or thin, as it lacks in strength and intensity due to insufficient amplitude of the sound waves.

Musical sounds in speech, as in music, are dependent upon a proper blending of quality, pitch and volume of tone. The German word *Klangefarbe,* meaning musical tone or tone color is a good description of that which we have attempted to describe. The human voice possesses a surprising range, when compared with other musical instruments, and an educated ear can do much to improve the fundamental quality of the speaking voice. Tone deafness or lack of musical ear makes it very difficult to secure the coöperation of the patient himself in improving his voice, when it is defective in any of these musical characteristics.

References.

1. APPELT. *Stammering and Its Permanent Cure.* London, 1911.
2. BLEUMEL. *Stammering and Cognate Defects of Speech.* Stechert, 1913.
3. BLANTON. *The Medical Significance of Speech Defects.* J. A. M. A. July 30, 1921, P. 373.
4. CORIAT. *Stammering as a Psychoneurosis.* J. Abn. Psychol. IX. 6, '15.
5. COEN. *Sprachanomalien.* Vienna, 1886.
6. DEARBORN, LORD CARMICHAEL. *Special Disabilities in Learning to Read and Write.* Stud. in Educa. Psychol. Harvard Univ., Cambridge, June, 1925.
7. GREENE, J. S. *Disorders of Speech.* Macmillan Company, N. Y. 1927, 458 p.
8. GUTZMANN, A. *Das Stottern.* Berlin, 1910.
9. KUSSMAUL. *Ziemssen's Cyc. of Medicine, XIV.* Chap. 1-8, 1877.
10. LIEBMANN. *Vorlusungen Aber Sprachstorungen.* Berlin, 1899.
11. MAKUEN, G. H. *Diagnosis and Treatment of Some Functional Forms of Defective Speech.* Philadelphia Medical Journal. 1901, VII, P. 25.
12. MARTIN, F. *Manual of Speech Training.* Ithaca, N. Y. 1926.
13. NADOLECZNY, MAX. *Diseases of Children.* Lippincott, 1914.
14. OSNATO. *Aphasia and Associated Speech Problems.* Hoebner, 1920.
15. SCRIPTURE. *Stuttering and Lisping.* Macmillan, 1914.
16. SCRIPTURE, M. K. *Speech Conflict, Jour. of Nev. & Ment. Dis.* XLII, 1, Jan., 1916.
17. SOUTHARD. *Shell Shock and Neuropsychiatry.* Leonard, Boston, 1919.
18. SWIFT, W. B. *Speech Defects in School Children.* Houghton-Mifflin, 1919.
19. TERMAN. *The Measurement of Intelligence.* Houghton-Mifflin, Boston, 1916. pp. 128-136.
20. TOWN, C. H. *Language Development in 285 Idiots and Imbeciles.* Psych. Clinic, Phil., 1913. pp. 229-35.
21. TREDGOLD. *Mental Deficiency.* Wm. Wood, 1916. Pp. 128-416.
22. VILLIGER. *Brain and Spinal Cord.* (Piersol), J. B. Lippincott Co., Phil., 1912.
23. WALLIN. *Theories of Stuttering.* Journ. Appl. Psychol. Dec., 1917.
24. WEAVER and O'NEILL. *Elements of Speech, The.* Longmans, Green & Co., N. Y.
25. WYLLIE, JOHN. *Disorders of Speech.* Oliver & Boyd, Edinburg, 1894.

Chapter III

THE RELATION OF SPECIAL DE-
FECTS TO SOCIAL MAL-
ADJUSTMENT

The Social Nature of Speech.

WHILE the early speech of the child is largely in-
dividualistic and ego-centric in character, it gradually
becomes more socialized and expressive of inner states,
moods, attitudes and beliefs. Rote-learning, parrot-
like repetition of adult speech sounds, is gradually replaced by meaningful sounds, to the end that the child
may more adequately control his environment, through
social intercourse. Speech is thus a "conditioned response", whose nature depends very largely upon the
social setting. Whereas primitive man had to evolve a
vocabulary gradually, the modern child finds a ready-
made vocabulary at hand, with a surprising number
of speech forms waiting for him, and he must acquire
a great many more words during the first years of his
existence than early primitive men found necessary
during an entire lifetime.

The nature of the social response in the individual
depends upon (1) that which stimulates him to *make*
a response, and (2) the responses which are made to
his own acts. Thus, according to Allport (1) language
is a "series of circular responses". Behind the act itself is some drive or idea more important than mere
imitation. The little girl spends her pennies for candy,
instead of putting them in the bank, because she wishes

to give pleasure to some other little girl; the boy carries the teacher's books because he wishes to secure
approval, or to appear "grown up".

Speech and Environment.

THE factors of environment, early training, intelligence of parents and social conditions generally have
not been sufficiently considered in discussions regarding the psychology of early language development. The
pathology of speech based on reports made in numer-
ous case history studies by speech specialists has shown
that an early speech handicap frequently alters the
character, personality and power of adaptation of an
individual. (17)

It is probable that the reason we speak of some individuals in society as men or women of "strong personality" is because they possess qualities of leadership in a high degree and are equipped with sufficient
intelligence, ability to profit by experience, foresight
and emotional control, to enable them to adapt very
successfully to the social conditions of their group and
to other groups outside their own immediate environment. Such a person is the "ward-boss", the capital-
ist, the social dictator, the man or woman in any walk
of life who leads by virtue of these qualities or special
gifts which constitute "personality" of the socially desirable type. (1)

Speech and Intelligence.

TOO great intelligence and too little intelligence seem
to disqualify for leadership. It has been found that
the child with an I. Q. of 160 or above is often a
poor mixer, regarded as "queer" by his contempora-

ries, and non-adaptive. In other words, such a person fails to adjust himself to the average level of the society about him, if he is far above the average in intelligence; if he is below the average, so that he is considered a dull-normal, or if mentally deficient with an I. Q. below 70, he has not sufficient intelligence to manage his own affairs successfully. *Human* elements are necessary for mass-control, for leadership and for popularity. Intelligence needs to be combined with cheerfulness, sense of humor, unselfishness, altruism, favorable temperament, forcefulness and distinction in bearing, in size or in appearance, in order to enable the person who would be a leader, to succeed in managing people, whether it be before the footlights, across the lecture platform, in the class-room, or in other forms of forensic art. The possession of a combination of these desirable qualities enables a person to attain to leadership more easily than can one without them.

Clear-cut, definite speech reactions and pleasing personalities are increasingly in demand in every profession. Social ease, linguistic ability, good appearance and character are recognized in many walks of life as extremely important factors in choosing an applicant. On the other hand, a speech defect may prove to be a serious economic as well as a social handicap.

The Speech of the College Girl.

It has been a matter of some concern and of no little interest to find that among the girls at Mount Holyoke College, where for six years speech tests have been given at the beginning of the Freshman year, those whose names appear in the speech correction group are often those who have difficulty also in making a satisfactory adjustment to college life and to college work. They rarely appear on Phi Beta Kappa lists and are seldom prominent in college athletics or in social life. It might seem that they were inferior in intelligence; but this is not the case, for according to the Psychological tests given also at college entrance, we find as many girls of good intelligence in the corrective group, as we do in the superior speech groups. In the matter of scholarship, however, we must admit that the corrective group contains a larger number of girls who have failed in the first semester of their Freshman year, or at some point during their college careers. These girls do not bear out in college work the promise of their psychological entrance examination. (14)

This leads us to inquire as to the reason for this maladjustment, since it is apparently not an intellectual handicap. Case histories yield such indicators as emotional instability, faulty home training, organic or functional disturbances of a supposedly trivial nature, psychotic tendencies of long years' standing, or personal peculiarities which account for many of the failures in adjustment to the social and academic work of the college. Whether the speech disturbance bears a causal relation to the maladjustment, or whether it is only one of the factors which become associated with feelings of failure, social inadequacy, and inefficiency in performance, it is difficult to say. It is apparent that the more intelligent girls, and those who appear off-hand to be more normal, alert, prepossessing and socially adjustive, also make the better social adaptation to college life and to academic standards. (15)

The question has been raised whether the special corrective group falls noticeably below a superior speech group in attainment in physical condition and in college work. In order to meet this inquiry we have analyzed much material from various departments for the year 1926-27, covering a superior speech group and the corrective group tested in the fall of 1926.

We found that the physical condition of the special group differed very little from that of the superior group. The special (corrective) group shows a somewhat greater tendency to certain respiratory diseases, frequent colds, influenza and tonsilitis, while in the superior group a larger number of tonsilectomies had been performed. This seems to indicate that the oral hygiene of the superior group is somewhat better at college entrance. Both groups show an equal susceptibility to the common diseases of childhood, according to available medical records.

The following table shows the scores of the two groups in the College Entrance Examinations and in the Psychological Examination given at college entrance. (16)

Table I

MEDIAN SCORES

	Special Group	Superior Group
1. College Entrance Examinations	71.8	77.3
2. Scholastic Aptitude Tests	543 points	544 points

No. 2 above shows the two groups to be about equal on general intelligence factors, but No. 1 indicates that in actual performance, under test conditions, the superior group maintains its superiority over the special group.

Table II shows the standing of the special speech group and the superior group in the Blanton-Stinchfield Speech

Measurements, and in the Seashore Music Tests (test for musical talent). The mean average for the special group is 106.6, while that of the superior group is 111.0. In the Seashore Tests for Musical Talent the special group made an average grade of C minus, while the superior speech group averaged C.

Table II

Rating in Speech Tests and in Tests for Musical Talent

MEDIAN SCORES

	Special Group	Superior Group
Speech Index in Objective Measurements .	13	15
Subjective Rating by Examiner	14	17
Articulation Test A	93	97
Articulation Test B	93	98
Oral Reading (Words per minute) . . .	184	180
Silent Reading (Words per minute) . . .	274	294
Spontaneous Speech Rate	120	132
Relevant Words Used in Spontaneous Speech	95%	96%
Vocabulary	74	72*
Average	106.6	111.0
Scores on Seashore Music Tests	C—	C

(The highest score in the whole group was B.)

The scores in Oral Reading are too close to make distinctions. Both groups attained a faster rate than that used by the best radio broadcasters, lecturers and public speakers. The median score for all students during the last four years has been between 170-190 words per minute in Oral Reading, and the median shown in Table II. lies within this range. The Mount Holyoke median for silent reading for four years has

*Vocabulary median of each group is above Terman's norm which is 65.

been 200-300 words per minute, and the table shows that the rate of these groups is within this range. By timing various radio lecturers we have found that they usually average between 120 and 140 words per minute. The Bible is often read at the rate of 90 to 100 words per minute, the rate occasionally slowing to about 75 words per minute. President Coolidge in his inaugural address maintained an average rate of 96-108 words per minute. In his Washington's Birthday Address (1927) his range was 96 to 120 words per minute with an average rate of 108 words per minute in various samplings taken every few moments during his speech. (16)

Southern girls tested at Mount Holyoke have a faster average rate in speech than have western or northern girls, but no generalizations are justified because we have tested only a small number. In ordinary conversation we find the rate faster than in platform speech and oratory, and generally faster than the rate for speakers upon the stage, altho only a small number of the latter seem to have been tested as to speed. Too frequently the speaker carries over the "colloquial" manner of speaking or weak form, so called, into his formal or platform address; and this may account for many of the inferior speeches given.

Speech and Social Adjustments.

HEALY (10) has called attention to the influence of speech defects upon the personality, and has found a number of cases in which stuttering has led to anti-social reactions on the part of the youth. In a number of cases speech disturbances seem to lie at the root of the maladjustment, leading to choice of undesirable companions, and eventually to juvenile delinquencies. Lacking the ability to cultivate companions within their own social group, they turn to companions of a less desirable sort, become suggestible and easily won to anti-social acts, because only in this way do they feel that they can assert their ego-instincts, and win recognition of however questionable a type. Thieving, vagrancy, run-away trips and homosexual practices have been indulged in by such boys and girls.

The character deterioration of the speech defective has been remarked by workers in speech pathology. Freud long ago called attention to the significance of unworthy thoughts and their tendency to crop out in "slips of speech". (5) One theory to account for the difficulty of the stutterer, is based on Freud's work. Psycho-analysts are convinced that unworthy thoughts, unsocial actions and the necessity for concealment lead to the initiation of stuttering, and that after many repetitions, the complex remaining, the speech becomes habitually hesitant, halting and blocked. The search for a cause may lead one back to infancy and to an unconscious system of ideas; bringing these hidden "complexes" to the surface and analyzing away the elements of the conflict will often relieve the symptoms, and eventually enable the stutterer to overcome his impediment. (4)

Healy (11) thinks that stuttering and other defects of speech may be signs of degeneracy or of defective traits. Very often an individual may be of normal intelligence, but in linguistics and in speech generally as well as in character traits show special handicaps which set him apart from his group. A favorable environment has frequently enabled a stutterer to overcome his handicap early in life. In a number of cases, individuals have attained a high degree of success in business or professional life in spite of the handicap of stuttering, but none of these individuals deny that the speech handicap has in some way proved a disadvantage, and an impediment, and that they might have been more successful without it. The stutterer in whom habits of delinquency have become established has usually been the butt of jokes, jibes and jeers. Eventually this has bred discouragement, indifference to the attainment of a successful career by the ordinary method and a perverted desire to obtain the "limelight" and to find some personal satisfaction, by socially undesirable methods.

Speech Therapy.

THERAPY in such cases must include daily "stints" of work in which some measure of success may be realized so that consciousness of deficiency may not be continually experienced. If possible, too close association with others should be avoided for a time, and farming, camp-life or out-door work sought wherever possible. Not too much attention should be directed to the speech itself. Emphasis should be upon physical upbuilding, good mental outlook, cheerful horizon and healthy attitudes.

Neuropathic disorders are found among certain races in a surprisingly large proportion. The number of Jewish boys who stutter has been commented upon by various writers. In such cases we often find minor nervous ailments such as habit spasms, chorea, great restlessness, nervous-anxious reactions and apprehension. When such nervousness reaches the stage of an anxiety neurosis, it is not surprising that stuttering should result.

Bisch (2) calls attention to the following "handi-caps of normality" found among many children, prac-tically all of which are remedial. Many of the handi-caps are closely related to speech defects.

1. Errors of refraction.
2. Chorea; habit spasms.
3. Speech defects.
4. Neurotic make-up.
5. Psychoneurosis (hysteria; neurasthenia; psychasthenia; compulsion neurosis, anxiety neurosis, etc.)
6. Psychopathic personality.
7. Specialized defects.
8. Irregular school attendance (training; wanderlust; illness.)
9. Unfavorable environment (home; associates; institu-tions, etc.)

Examples of Speech Handicaps.

STUTTERING is frequently found among precocious children, and is probably due to over-stimulation, un-due excitement, faulty home training, or imitation of a stuttering relative. A small boy of ten years recently referred by his mother because of the onset of stutter-ing, was found to be well developed physically, and with no organic cause for his difficulty. His father was not living and the child was one of three, the brother and sister having no speech difficulty but all being highly excitable, tense, nervous and temperamental. The mother was a very rapid speaker, with some ner-vous mannerisms which the boy imitated. His speech was the direct result of imitative tendencies and the stuttering was easily overcome in a few weeks by special training, and by coöperation within the home. This boy was alert, attentive and precocious in intelligence. Every stutterer found at Mount Holyoke, during a period of six years has been well above average in intelligence.

Healy (10) mentions a deaf mute whose delinquency is traceable to dissatisfaction and feelings of inferiority, associated with unsuccessful social attempts. This boy became a "constitutional psychopathic inferior" and a trouble maker. The physical difficulty in this case was mutism; he was a son of deaf-mutes. His physical development was poor, his sex development premature, his mentality keen, but *emotionally* he was unstable, irritable, excitable, obstinate and changeable, without emotional control. He was arrested for obtaining money under false pretenses.

The writer knows a stutterer whose speech difficulty went back to unfortunate childhood experiences, disillusionment and sex knowledge gained in an undesirable way. He was unable to find companionship and coöperation in the home to help him overcome his difficulty, because of the temperamental, domineering attitude of his father, a brilliant professional man, but without understanding or sympathy for his adolescent son. Fearing to face his father at the end of the year after a failure in certain high school subjects, he ran away from home.

Healy (11) mentions another case in which a language defect, coupled with disability in reading, writing and spelling led to delinquency charges. (3) This boy was in a poor systemic condition, physically, and was subject to sick headaches. His social adaptation had always been faulty and there had been difficulty at home and in school. Disobedience, truancy and running away from home resulted.

The effect of a speech defect upon the personality

of the individual ranges from mild inferiority feeling, to deep depression and suicidal tendencies. Not only is this true of stutterers but of those who possess other speech handicaps such as lisping, peculiar vocal quality and the like. The following are mentioned as cases which have come to our attention as speech correction problems within the past few years.

Case I.   Problem; stuttering and nervousness; habit spasms. Physical factors; left-handedness. Motor coördination poor; facial "tics". Emotional factors; Excitable, over-reacting and noisy. Speech; stuttering and lisping. Assigned to speech correction group. Scholarship about average during first year. Improved during college course; eventually became an excellent student in two departments. Bi-weekly half-hour conferences given for first semester of Freshman year; weekly conferences for second semester; infrequent conferences and social "visits" during balance of college course. Speech showed improvement during first semester; but decided improvement was not apparent in home and college until beginning of second year. Gradually eliminated facial spasms, facial grimaces, extraneous muscle movements such as finger movements, eye muscles, etc. Improved motor coördination, with development of poise, ease and freedom in speech and in general adjustment to social and academic life. Seniors associating with her for the first time were unaware that she had ever stuttered. At the outset this was one of the most difficult cases which we have found in the college, but the girl's own attitude, her determination, coöperation, the home attitude, friendship with a coöperative upperclass girl, and good intelligence, enabled her to take advantage of the opportunity offered to help her to overcome her speech difficulty, before she left college. Upon graduation she obtained an appointment to one of the best positions offered to any girl in her class.

Case II.   Problem; Infantile lisp and tongue-tie. Physical factors; negative. Emotional factors; negative. Speech apparently based upon imitation within the home, as her sister lisped and mother had also lisped at one time. Parents resisted suggestion that the frenum be clipped to enable her to make accurate tongue contacts for the various speech sounds. In Junior year the girl decided to have this condition corrected, realizing the importance of good speech in teaching—her chosen profession. Speech work given in Senior year to follow up operative work and improvement noticeable. Unfortunate that treatment was delayed to her final year in college, as there was little time left for training before she was graduated. It is also unfortunate that the home coöperation was lacking at the outset.

Case III. Problem: Social maladjustment and feelings of inferiority associated with family background. Physical factors; Negative; not a robust girl however. Emotional factors; Repressed and having peculiarities; subject to moods; unsocial. Her speech was tense, repressed and of poor quality. Fear over approaching examinations aroused unusual reactions, seclusiveness, refusal of food and caused much worry to roommate and house matron. Conferences were given through contacts offered in her speech work, and she was able to go through the examination period, and take the dreaded examination in a certain subject. Although she failed the course, she went on for her sophomore year satisfactorily so far as her other work was concerned. Although eventually obliged to leave college, because of "condition" incurred in one subject, she became reconciled to the situation, finished certain units of her college work, and transferred happily to an institution offering another type of work, where she has progressed satisfactorily.

Case IV. Problem: Emotional attitude of the principals in a "girl-crush" affair, one of the individuals being in the speech correction group. The attentions of an upperclass girl brought an unfortunate over-attachment on the part of the Freshman, which unsettled her work, and interfered in various ways with her college adjustment. The upperclass girl was largely to blame in the affair. She was rather given to "crushes" with lowerclassmen and it is possible that the overstimulation due to over-activity of the thyroid glands may have been responsible for her demonstrativeness and craving for affection. There are undoubtedly more "over-attachments" of this sort between girls in a woman's college, than in a coeducational college or university, as in the latter place the friendships with men and the rivalry for their attentions make for normal social contacts. Over-attachments among girls may lead to a display of "emotional fire-works" in which the underclassman prides herself on "fagging" for the upperclassman, often taking time needed on her own work, to do favors for the upperclassman. Usually a change of dormitory is necessary before such an attachment settles to a normal level. The principals in these cases often consider themselves martyrs, and the breaking up of such a friendship often assumes all the importance of a disappointment in love.

Case V. Problem; stuttering. Physical factors; negative. Emotional factors; negative. Speech; seemed to be the result of nervousness and the possible inheritance of a constitutional handicap which led to stuttering. The mother had been a stutterer, and had never entirely overcome it, but had died while this child was small so that imitation was impossible. This girl requested to be allowed to work out her difficulty through taking the college work in dramatics, rather than through regular corrective work. She could repeat words in print without hesitation, and never hesitated on committed lines. Her spontaneous speech however was faulty, hesitant and repressive in type. She was excellent in college dramatics but showed little or no improvement in spontaneous speech. This indicates that training along artistic lines only is not the best way to overcome a coördination neurosis such as stuttering. Individual drill, some study of the individual, and special exercises suited to the individual needs are needed in addition to platform work and dramatics, for stutterers.

Case VI. Problem; stuttering: in 16 yr. old boy. Nationality; Jewish. Physical factors; Twenty pounds underweight, tall, over-grown in height, but gaunt and thin, emaciated in appearance. Intelligence quotient 125 or well above average.

Emotional factors; Negatively suggestible personality; stubborn and contrary to unusual degree. Home conditions favored development of this trait up to the time when speech training was begun. Referred because of speech defect and for failure in senior year in high school. Was placed in private school for the following year, and received frequent speech conferences and training. Improved, passing his school subjects and is preparing now to take the college board examinations. Home situation improved and coöperation secured to enable him to do this. Speech continued improving altho stuttering still persists under certain conditions.

Case VII. Stutter and infantile lisp. 13 year old boy. Nationality; American. Good family background. Physical factors; negative. Emotional factors; Sensitive and rather feminine in reactions, easily hurt, being what the children call more or less of a "sissy" among boys. Stutter became noticeable during the school year when boys ridiculed him for his "baby-talk", and as the family did not know how to teach him to "talk plainly", the boy increased his difficulties by imposing a stutter upon his lisping sounds. Weekly lessons, home drill and coöperation enabled him to make noticeable improvement during the school year.

Overcoming Speech Handicaps.

WHILE the primary aim of corrective work in speech is to enable the individual to overcome a social and economic handicap sufficiently to remove a very tangible stumbling block in the way of success, there are now and then individuals who do much better than this. A girl with good intelligence may become interested not only in overcoming her difficulty but may even excel in interpretative work in college. A girl may come to college with an infantile, high-pitched, unformed voice perhaps handicapped with remnants of a lisp, and yet star in dramatics before she completes her college career; a girl with a lisp may improve sufficiently to take a poetry prize; a girl with a stutter may develop persistent attention, determination and aggressiveness which will win her a good position at the end of her college course. Girls first held for speech requirements in the Freshman year, because they are not up to a satisfactory standard, have, in a number of cases, represented the college in poetry reading contests, in debate, in recitals and in plays. The very fact that they had *something to overcome,* has in a number of cases served as a stimulus to creative work which has been above average, and this in itself is sufficient evidence of the importance of corrective work in schools and colleges.

This is not a task for the elocutionist, however, nor for the beginner in speech training. It demands a trained expert in the field of speech pathology, assisted by sympathetic colleagues in the departments of speech, physical education, hygiene and psychology, who can coöperate in the problems of adjustment and personality development. Individual conferences are more profitable than class drill in such instances, and short individual conferences seem better than full period conferences, provided they are not too far apart.

References.

1. ALLPORT. *Social Psychology.* Houghton-Mifflin Co., 1924, Pp. 169-198.
2. BISCH. *Clinical Psychology.* Williams & Wilkins, Baltimore, 1926, P. 64.
3. BRONNER. *Special Abilities and Disabilities, Psychology of.* Little, Brown & Co., Boston, 1917.
4. CORIAT. *Abnormal Psychology.* Moffat & Yard, N. Y., 1921, Pp. 381-383.
5. FREUD. *Psychopathology of Everyday Life.* Fisher-Unwin, Lond., 1917.
6. GESSELL. *Exceptional Children and Public School Policy.* Yale Univ. Press, 1921.
7. GODDARD. *Psychology of the Normal and Subnormal.* Dodd, Mead & Co., N. Y., 1919, Pp. 174-192.

8. HALL, G. S. *Youth, Its Education and Regime*. Appleton Co., N. Y., 1907.
9. HATFIELD. *Psychology and Morals*. Robt. McBride Co., 1926.
10. HEALY. *The Individual Delinquent*. Little, Brown & Co., Boston, 1922, Pp. 220-223.
11. IBID. Pp. 516-521.
12. MORGAN, J. J. *The Psychology of the Unadjusted School Child*. 1924.
13. PIAGET. *The Language and Thought of the Child*. Harcourt-Brace Co., 1926, P. 53.
14. STINCHFIELD. *Speech Defects as a Personnel Problem*. Jour. of Am. Speech, Dec., 1926.
15. IBID. *Some Relationships between Speech Defects, Musical Disability, Scholastic Attainment and Maladjustment*. Quar. Jour. Sp. Educ., June, 1927, Pp. 268-276.
16. IBID. *Expression as an Index to Intelligence*. Jour. of Expression, June, 1927, Pp. 8-14.
17. WEST, R. *Purposive Speaking*. Macmillan Co., N. Y., 1924, Pp. 34-41.
18. WILLIAMS, GESSELL, CAMPBELL, MYERSON, FERNALD, etc. *Special Aspects of Mental Hygiene*. Yale Univ. Press, 1925.

Chapter IV

NEUROTIC AND SUB-NORMAL CHILDREN

Feelings of Inferiority.

PEDIATRICIANS and Psychiatrists have called attention to the relation between organ inferiority and various speech defects. Feelings of inferiority are closely related to physical inferiority and Adler (1) has given us the term "constitutional psychopathic inferior" to cover certain pathological types in whom are found not only speech defects but other defects associated with organic and functional speech disturbances.

In the early years of childhood the boy and girl "hold the mirror up to nature" by copying the actions, gestures and words of those about them. Common words and actions have a dramatic significance to the small child. The child of foreign-born parents may pick up profanity and strange words or may perform unusual acts as a result of the novelty of the stimulus which he has received. The child adopts the accent and speech of his family first of all. If they speak a foreign language exclusively during the pre-school years, the child's acquirement of the English language may be deferred until he meets other children on the playgrounds or in school.

Attitude of the Home Towards the Child.

WITH a very sensitive or nervous child a speech disturbance may occur as a result of the struggle to learn the English language at the same time that he must use another language at home. This makes him very nervous and leads to confusion in speaking. It may even lead to stuttering. If elders in the home use a sharp, abrupt tone in dealing with children, it may cause them to be fearful, timid, or embarrassed in their reactions. This often leads to hesitant, uncertain manner and tone. Feelings of inferiority, timidity, pathological lying, habit spasms, sleeplessness, unsociability, mental peculiarities and moodiness may often be reactions to adults in the home who are responsible for the child's anxiety, irritability, maladjustment or psychotic tendencies. (3) The plasticity of the child's mind and ease of transition from one reaction to another enable him to learn during the first five years of life faster than at any other five-year period in life. This same sensitivity enables him to learn rapidly and too well those things which adults may be quite unconsciously teaching him by example. Adler has shown us that the presence of inferior organs demands special training of the nerve tracts in order that the child may compensate for his inferiority whenever possible in a socially desirable way. A poor digestive apparatus for instance may cause a child to be a gourmand or greedy to an extraordinary degree. The neurotic child is always the victim of his own inferiorities to a certain extent. His overt speech, implicit language habits and actions are therefore directly related to his feelings of inferiority. He may thus unfortunately be too much dominated by other children in the household.

In the case of one child in a family of six it was found that maladjustment within the family circle was chiefly responsible for a stuttering habit which was rapidly becoming worse. This boy had an older brother with an intelligence quotient of 125 and a younger sister also of a superior mental rating. The boy himself possessed an intelligence quotient of about 90 to 100 and was more lethargic in thought and action than were any of the other children in the family. He was often imposed upon by the more active brother and sister who put upon him certain chores, errands, and duties threatening to "get even" with him if the state of affairs were revealed to his father or mother. This treatment continued for some months and produced a sullen, moody disposition in the boy, with increasing resentment toward the brother and sister who were imposing upon him; nor did it add to his happiness to hear the mother and grandmother frequently praise his brother and sister in his hearing because of their "brilliancy." Even though it was not directly stated, he felt that by *implication* his family blamed him for his incompetency. The unhappy mental state and concealment of its cause, produced a hesitancy in speech, leading to stuttering in school and at home. When the matter was brought to the attention of his parents they were much concerned because of their own responsibility in adding to the boy's difficulty, and felt that it was best to send the older boy away to school for a time and to give the patient his chance. During the following year the boy's speech was surprisingly improved. He was able to do his school work satisfactorily, made an excellent adjustment within the household, and no longer found that his sister attempted to dominate him as she had done when the older brother was present.

In another instance a girl of nine who greatly admired a brother two years her elder imitated the actions of the brother in play and games and attempted to equal him in various sports and in mental per-

formances. This was found to be too difficult for her
and produced excitement and nerve tension which led
to stuttering. The brother conscious of his own superiority took advantage by teasing and annoying the girl
and it was not until he was sent away to school that his
sister recovered her mental and physical equilibrium.

Every Child an Individual Problem.

IN most families a solution of the problem must be
sought on some other basis than was found in the two
above mentioned cases as most children must be dealt
with at home and by their own parents. Parents must
therefore realize that children cannot all be dealt with
in the same manner; that every child presents its own
peculiar problems, and what may be right and good
for one child may not be best for another.

Attitude of Other Members of the Household.

OLDER children frequently over-stimulate younger
members of the household and while the younger ones
may talk earlier it must be remembered that such
stimulation sometimes leads to stuttering habits. The
Montessori method teaches children precision of
movement and control of the nerve centers through
motor coördination and the forming of desirable
habits. If parents would consider their own speech reactions, using the polite, calm, and agreeable tones of
voice which they desire the child to imitate, they
might expect the same speech "manners" to prevail
in the child. Rapidly spoken, jerky words, curt com-
mands and insistence upon obedience are too often the
characteristics which the child learns to associate with
the elders of the household. In speaking sharply to

children adults cause a child to become nervous, irritable and often to respond with a poor speech reaction. The child is able to understand language much easier than he can speak it, and adults forget in dealing with an infant that he interprets much from the tones of the voice and the expression of the countenance. A child of 18 months can be addressed in a reasonable practical manner so that he will understand what is being said. Certain physicians and nurses in children's hospitals testify to the fact that a very small baby will often cease to cry in response to a few pleasant words from a certain doctor or nurse. A child will develop a temper-tantrum less quickly if he understands the reason for certain things. If a sharp knife is taken from the child's hands, the mother may explain to him by gesture how painful may be the injury which a sharp instrument inflicts. If she hurriedly takes the knife and hides it away, she only increases his curiosity and dramatizes the action, so that the child is still unsatisfied until he experiments for himself.

Parental Guidance.

PATIENCE and persistence are important principles for parental practise in overcoming nervous and psychotic tendencies in children in various fields. They are equally important in the development of desirable speech habits and in overcoming the tendency to speak too rapidly, to lisp or to mumble words. Conflicts between parents and children are an unfortunate source of emotional difficulty which may lead to a failure to overcome faulty speech, such as lisping or stuttering. The "neurotic lisper" has been described elsewhere* and we know that children may remain infantile if

*Stuttering and Lisping, Macmillan Co., 1914, E. W. Scripture.

they can enlist the sympathy of adults more easily by baby talk, lisping or whining. They will continue to act thus, because they find it serviceable.

If a boy is brought up by a stern parent, or if he observes frequent struggles and disagreements between parents, he will either suffer disillusionment or develop fear of the outcome. This may result in a nervous, hasty manner, a furtive gesture; nervous fears and apprehension. Affection may be observed in the infant early in the first year, but too much caressing and handling is not good for the baby. A mother may cuddle and caress her infant too much, causing an over-attachment from which the child may extricate himself only with great difficulty in adulthood. The mother may sap the child's emotional energy to the detriment of his adult life. Children should be encouraged to be straightforward and to satisfy their curiosity in socially desirable ways as well as to manifest originality and inventiveness, and the family attitude plays an important part in all this. Too often we punish the child unreasonably for what the adult considers to be wrong, failing to show the child where he has erred and we make too little of him for doing well, when he deserves praise. Adults misunderstand children quite as frequently as children misunderstand adults. Because of this fact we have many neurosis in adult life which are traceable to the repressions and complexes of childhood. It is for this reason that we find many nervous, over-stimulated children in families well above the poverty-line and often among those of superior intelligence. Freud (11) calls attention to the fact that the habit of forgetting, so common to childhood, may hold the key to our understanding of certain amnesias at the basis of neurotic symptoms in

adult life. Childhood experiences are often unconsciously lived over again or reënacted.

A small Austrian boy accompanied his mother to
this country. The mother was exceedingly unhappy as
she had been deserted by her husband and had come
to this country to try to find him. She talked much to
the boy about the unsettled family conditions, and of
her fear lest she be unable to make a living for them.
The boy was not robust physically and became anxious
and unhappy over the situation. He could speak only
the Austrian language when placed in the public
schools of America. A few days after coming to this
country he was chased by a barking dog when on his
way to school, and a paroxysm of fear was produced.
In his excitement and fear he developed a severe stutter, in trying to tell his teacher what had happened,
and for months thereafter the nervous state per-
sisted. Even after the cessation of his fear, the stuttering symptom remained.

Stuttering and stammering may be forms of mental
confusion or lack of clear thinking. We are all familiar with the "slips of speech" which come about sometimes in embarrassment.

Mistakes in reading and writing are (11) common
examples. We often forget appointments we do not
wish to keep or are late for disagreeable duties. We
are usually prompt for any affair which we anticipate
with pleasure. Thus forgetting is sometimes called a
disturbance of thought due to a conflict, or disagreeable system of ideas.

Certain defects in speech and various other actions
such as "tics" or unnecessary habit-movements, such
as playing with a watch chain, biting one's finger-nails,
handling clothing, etc. are regarded as symptomatic.

The psychiatrist of the present day is calling our attention to the study of abnormal psychology, the effect of the subconscious mind, childhood training, and environment upon adult reactions. We have considered mental disorders only in so far as they seem related to speech disabilities. Certain speech symptoms are present in various mental diseases as in dementia praecox. The speech-pressure accompanying the manic phase of manic-depressive insanity and the absence of speech in the depressive phase are sometimes early symptoms of the disease long before it has taken a more active form. Mental disorders and speech defects accompany paresis and may be the first symptoms of its presence.

The Psychosis.

ON the affective side the normal individual is often subject to emotional outbursts due to terror, anger, revenge, or despair. If it is of fairly long duration we speak of it as a *mood*. If it is continuous and dominates a personality it is called *temperament*. The normal person is adjusted to his environment and passively or actively reacts to his surroundings or extends his horizon. The psychotic individual may fail to make a desirable adjustment within his environment, may feel economically and socially inferior and may become a menace or even threaten human life. Such a person flees from reality to seek refuge in a dream life and to substitute dreams for action.

According to White (24) the neurosis and the psychosis are symbols of unsatisfied instinctive desires translated into motor attitudes which may be appropriate for fulfilling them but which, because of conflicting ideals, cannot find an outlet in action.

"Insanity" has been defined as a form of social inadequacy which may be expressed in any one of a number of mental diseases. Under the head of psychosis mentioned by White (24) the following are accompanied by speech symptoms, which are often significant to the trained worker and physician.

1 Paranoia

2 Manic-Depressive Psychosis

3 Paresis

4 Dementia Praecox

5 Senile Psychosis

6 Toxic Psychosis

7 Borderland States

8 Idiocy and Imbecility

The Psychoneurosis.

THIS term refers primarily to functional disorders of the nervous system and presents a better prognosis than we find in the psychosis. The individual may react normally, and may not become particularly unsocial or peculiar, nor need to be taken away from his accustomed environment, so far as his family can determine. Such a person may however, be suffering from a mild mental break-down, or from some form of maladjustment such as (1) neurasthenia, (2) psychasthenia or (3) hysteria.

Neurasthenia.

IN *neurasthenia* we find a strong fatigue element and increased susceptibility to it. Here one often finds active worry, anxiety, fear and inability to concentrate. While this disorder was rare among men in the ranks during the world war it was quite common among officers.

Psychasthenia.

THE symptoms of *psychasthenia* are fatigue, sleeplessness, poor appetite, scattered attention, lack of concentration, and often great mental distress.

Hysteria

THE hysterical temperament may be frequently observed in advanced life. The hysterical person is unstable emotionally, sensitive, and egotistical, craving sympathy, admiration and attention but unable to win them by ordinary means. The hysteric will go to great lengths to be the center of attention. Hysteria has been defined as "the conversion of a mental conflict into a physical symptom". It is more common among women than among men but a great many cases occurred during the World War and have been discussed by Southard (20) under the head of hysterical blindness, hysterical deafness, amnesia, aphasia, stuttering and other disturbances of speech and personality.

The neurotic person is divided against himself, he cannot make decisions. *Euphoria,* or the state of wellbeing, common to the normal well-balanced personality gives way to *abulia* or a state of suspended activity, moodiness and indecision. In this state the inner nature wages eternal conflict and the person is unable to make clean-cut, practical decisions and to stand by them. Such a personality is often found in the stutterer and just as other hysterical personalities are sometimes speedily cured by suggestion, the hysterical stutterer is frequently cured of his speech defect if it is taken in time.

Our attention has been called to the importance of an early recognition of nervous disorders among college students. Williams (25) contends that happiness and efficiency depend upon mental as well as upon physical factors. When students are faced with the necessity of making their own decisions and settling

issues when those about them have different standards
from those in which they were reared, it is difficult
for them to decide what to do. To students away from
home for the first time such matters as social contacts, embarrassment, awareness of shortcomings,
attitude towards the family, money matters, clothes,
and fear of failure sometimes form the basis of anxiety states which lead to neurosis. The physical condition of students now receives considerable attention,
but the "psychic scars" leave deep wounds which may
be very important in college adjustments. It is difficult
to determine whether speech defects stand in a causal
relationship to social maladjustment, but the frequency with which emotional difficulties and maladjustments occur in the speech corrective groups points
to the conclusion that there is rather an intimate relationship between maladjustments, and speech defects.

The Sub-Normal Child (22).

IN the field of clinical psychology we find abundant
references to the speech defects of the mentally deficient child. Clinicians have found it easy to diagnose
such varieties of amentia, as cretanism, epilepsy, idiocy, imbecility and the like. *These* cases may be segre-
gated, properly cared for and protected from unscru-
pulous individuals. Society will then be protected from
acts due to the mental deficiency of these individuals.
Mild mental and physical anomalies present a much
more difficult problem than merely the diagnosis and
disposition of the case. In the typical border-line case
perhaps not one of the special intellectual functions is
entirely lacking; memory may be good, sensory equip-
ment normal, physical functions good, and yet beha-

vior problems appear and the child is unable to profit by experience. Often emotional handicaps accompany a certain dullness in mentality which makes it impossible for us to classify these cases with assurance.

There is usually a general lowering of the mental level in the case of the border-line child, which may be shown in performance tests. It remains for us to determine the cause, to establish the present level, and to decide what training, environment, or discipline should be given to the child in question. Will he be able to adjust himself successfully in the world at large or should he be placed in a special institution? By success we do not refer to the ability to amass wealth; to show genius or even to be considered entirely socially adjustable. We refer rather to his ability to work under supervision, to be trusted, to perform some useful work passably well, to be partially or wholly self-supporting and to be intrusted with some degree of responsibility. He may then engage in activities in society rather than be rigidly supervised at home or within an institution.

In other words the border-line child is one who has intelligence enough to earn his own living, to conform in some degree to the ordinary demands of society, and to acquire the special training which fits his level of performance.

A large number of children suffering from such handicaps as blindness, deafness, and deformity are found to have a mental handicap also. In the schools for the blind the mental level of children now entering these institutions seems on the whole to be lower than it was a number of years ago. This is probably due to improved medical supervision and the prevention of blindness by treatment of the eyes of children at birth.

A large number of mentally deficient children are brought to every speech clinic and it is sometimes a rather difficult matter for clinical workers to determine whether the child is sufficiently intelligent to warrant spending a great deal of time and energy upon speech education. There are so many normal children in public schools having speech defects that it is always a question whether the speech teacher should expend time and energy upon the speech of the deficient or sub-normal child. There is no question that teachers in opportunity classes, special classes for sub-normal and backward children, should have special training in speech correction and phonetics in order to improve the speech of children whom they teach. The results obtained would give satisfaction to teacher and pupils and content the parents, when perhaps the improvement might be so slight that a special speech teacher would not be willing to undertake the task.

Intelligence is an hereditary factor and Goddard (13) found that mental defect can also be frequently traced to heredity. Native ability seems to be fixed by inheritance within certain limits, beyond which the individual cannot pass, whatever the training, education, or environment, acquired. Learning and training however, may discover special aptitudes in children and enable them to utilize to better advantage the intelligence which they possess.

Degrees of Intelligence.

AMONG the feeble-minded, the child or adult whose mental age is 1-2 years is called an idiot. One whose mental level is between 3-7 years is called an imbecile. One with a mental age of 8-12 is of moron intelligence, according to Goddard's classification. Terman (21) in his examination of one thousand children called sixteen years the upper limit for average adult intelligence but the Army Alpha and Beta tests given to 80,000 during the World War shows that fourteen years is the probable upper limit for the civilian population. The mental tests run as high as the 18 year level, the person passing the 18 year test being classed as a superior individual.

The following table is given by Woodworth for all children;—(27):

I.Q.	below 70	1%	Feeble-minded.
I.Q.	70–79	5%	Border-line Mentality.
I.Q.	80–89	14%	Dull-Normal.
I.Q.	90–99	30%	Average Intelligence.
I.Q.	100–109	30%	" or slightly above.
I.Q.	110–119	14%	Above average, or superior.
I.Q.	120–129	5%	Very superior.
I.Q.	Over 129	1%	Exceedingly superior.

Goddard (12) and Dugdale (9) find that many criminals are mentally inferior. From the standpoint of Speech training it is important to know that whenever there is a lesion in the motor speech center very little can be done to improve the speech. Also, when deafness accompanies the mental defect speech training is of very little use. Children of the idiot level speak rarely if at all, having no ideas to express beyond those which may may be shown by primitive gesture language or inarticulate sounds. In milder degrees of mental deficiency some speech is present but it is usually mutilated, imperfect and does not yield readily to corrective methods. Tredgold (22) attributes the speech deficiency to abnormalities of the sensory receptive organs or to motor deficiencies within the central nervous system which interfere with normal muscular control and coördination. Such incoördination is expressed in stuttering, oral inaccuracies, mutations, slurring speech and letter substitutions. In the higher grades of mental deficiency corrective work often yields satisfactory results.

In the mentally deficient child speech is often delayed beyond the period when it is present in the normal child. The language of the mentally deficient child is an important index of the grade of mentality. The normal child forms associations between objects and their names about the end of the first year. The deficient child may be five, six or even older before he begins to form these associations and attach names to objects. It may be even later before he can form sentences. Defects of speech in the mentally deficient child may be due to lesions in the sensory, motor, or association areas of the brain.

Ashby (2) finds that slurring, lalling and lisping in a child of five or six years is very frequently associated with defective or sub-normal mentality.

Doctor Lapage (15) finds the following consonantal defects among feeble-minded children.

Consonant.	Letter Substitution	Example
1. Most	k	t	tat (cat)
frequently	g	d	dun (gun)
defective	ng	d	strind (string)
	t	d	deef (teeth)
	d	t	toor (door)
	n	d	dose (nose)
	p	t-d	dader (paper)
	b	p	pag (bag)
	m	b	jab (jam)
	f	t	tottee (coffee)
	v	b	belbet (velvet)
	s	t	tissors (scissors)
	z	dse	nodse (nose)
	sh	tsh, t	tsheep (sheet)
	th	f, t, d	fumb (thumb)
	r	y, l	yabbit (rabbit) labit
	y	r, l	lellow (yellow)
	l	y	yeg (leg)
	w	m	mindow (window)

In a series of speech tests given at the Belchertown State School for the Feebleminded in June 1927, in which eleven of the children of the better mental level were tested, ten out of the eleven had speech which was sufficiently poor to be classified under *speech defects*. Practically all of these were remedial, because of the fact that the mental level was such that the children could profit by instruction. (See Table No. I.)

Table I

TABLE showing error frequencies on various consonants in initial, middle or final position among 11 children in the State School for the Feeble-minded,* Belchertown, Mass.

In initial position	Substitution given	mid. position	Substitution	Final position	Substitution	Numbers refer to error frequencies
f (2)		f (1)		f (6)	v, p	
v (6)	b and w					
th (8) (voiceless)	fr; fw; t					
th (9) (voiced)	d					
s (9)	th; ts					
z (9)	th; dse					
sh (6)	th or s					
zh (8)	thz, dz					
ch (6)	s; ts					
j (4)	d					
r (4)	w					
x (ks) (4)	th					
l (6)	y or w	1		1 (omitted)		
k (3)	t					
g (3)	ch					
ng (8)	n or d					
t (1)	d					
d (2)	t					
n (1)	d					
y (2)	l					
h (2)	(omitted)					
m (1)	b (oral instead of nasal sound given.)					

Consonant Combinations (mutations, substitutions, etc.)

gl (2)	gw
bl (4)	bw
fl (3)	fw
pl (3)	pw
sl (1)	sw
tr (2)	tw
gr (9)	gw
br (2)	bw
mbr (1)	bwe (in word *umbrella*) gave "bwe" for entire word.
sl (1)	sw
sp (7)	thp
skw (8)	kw (in word *squirrel*)
lz (6)	lth

Table II

Table showing types of speech difficulty among 11 feeble-minded children.

Lisping	40%
Letter Substitution	30%
Stuttering	10%
Nasality	20%
Total	100%

Numerals in Table I refer to error frequencies (i.e., *9 errors* mean that 9 children out of 11 had difficulty with given sound).   *Studied by the author.

References.

1. ADLER. *The Neurotic Constitution.* Moffat, Yard & Co., 1921.
2. ASHBY, H. *Speech Defects in Mentally Deficient Children.* Med. Chron., Oct., 1903.
3. BLANTON. *Speech Training for Children.* Century Co., 1919.
4. BINET-SIMON. *The Development of Intelligence in Children.* Pub. of Tr. Sch., Vineland, N. J., No. 11, May, 1916.
5. CAMERON, H. C. *The Nervous Child.* Oxford Medical Pub. Co., London, 1923.
6. CAMPBELL, C. M. *Mental Disorders.* Harvard Univ. Press, 1924.
7. CHURCH AND PETERSON. *Nervous and Mental Diseases.* W. B. Saunders Co., Phila.
8. CORIAT, I. *Abnormal Psychology.* Moffat, Yard & Co., N. Y., 1921.
9. DUGDALE, R. L. *The Jukes.* N. Y., 1902 (Part I, Chap. 8), Pp. 67-70, 1911.
10. FRANZ, S. I. *Handbook of Mental Examination Methods.* Nervous and Mental Disease Publishing Co., Washington.
11. FREUD, S. *The Psycho-Pathology of Every Day Life.* Macmillan Co., 1893.
12. GODDARD, H. H. *Four Hundred Feeble-minded Children Classified by The Binet Method.* Ped. Sem. 17; 1910, pp. 387-397.
13. GODDARD, H. *The Kallikak Family.* Nerv. & Ment. Disease Pub. Co., Washington, D. C.
14. KEMPF, E. J. *The Autonomic Functions and the Personality.* Nerv. & Ment. Dis. Pub. Co., Washington, D. C.
15. LAPAGE, C. P. *Feeble-mindedness in Children.*
16. MURCHISON, CARL. *Criminal Intelligence.* Clark Univ. Press, Worcester.
17. NADOLECZNY, M. *Diseases of Children.* J. P. Lippincott, 1914.
18. PRATT, G. K. (et al). *The Mental Hygiene Primer.* Massachusetts Ment. Hyg. Soc., Boston.
19. RIGGS. *Nervousness and its Prevention.* P. 284.
20. SOUTHARD. *Shell Shock and Neuropsychiatry.* Leonard Pub. Co., Boston, 1919.
21. TERMAN, L. *The Measurement of Intelligence.* Houghton Mifflin Co., Boston.
22. TREDGOLD. *Mental Deficiency.* William Wood Co., N. Y., 1916, pp. 128, 416.
23. WELLS, F. L. *Mental Tests in Clinical Practice.* World Book Co., 1927.
24. WHITE, W. A. *Outlines of Psychiatry.* Nerv. & Ment. Dis. Pub. Co., 1921.
25. WILLIAMS, F. K. *Mental Hygiene and the College Student.* Mass. Ment. Hyg. Soc., Boston.
26. WILLIAMS, T. *Dreads and Besetting Fears.* Little, Brown & Co., Boston, 1923.
27. WOODWORTH, R. S. *Psychology.* Henry Holt & Co., 1921, pp. 271, 293.

Part II

Chapter V

SPEECH MEASUREMENT

MENTAL measurements began to arouse interest in this country about 1890. Kraepelin's work in Germany on methods of diagnosis for use with insane and mentally abnormal patients gave a great impetus to it. Binet's work in the schools of Paris, about 1905-08 furnished a basis for segregating mentally deficient children. Further research in individual and social psychology has made possible the development of a wide range of psychological measurements, such as trade tests, tests of the emotional life, measures of general intelligence. Special abilities and disabilities have been given attention only within the last part of the first quarter of this century. Methods of diagnosis in reading, writing, spelling and arithmetic are in use in many schools of today.

The development of a special technique for testing the speech of school children is relatively new. Alice Descoeudres of Geneva (8) made one of the early attempts in this field, trying to find a form for children of each age level. Hers were entirely tests of intelligence. She found an important social difference in the language development of children in uneducated classes as compared with children of the educated classes. From the standpoint of intelligence findings, her tests are important, but they give no standards or guidance for determining the nature of the speech handicap, such as stuttering, oral inaccuracies, lisping, or letter substitution.

Speech surveys have been given in several large

cities of the United States, but on the whole, very little practical help has been derived from them, as differences in method and procedure render them difficult to compare. In order to aid in the diagnosis of speech disturbances and to assist in their gradual elimination, a standardized speech test or series of graded tests seemed essential. A properly graded scale could be used by teachers of speech and diagnosticians generally. The Blanton-Stinchfield Speech Measurements (3) were therefore undertaken at the University of Wisconsin, to provide a practical means of measuring speech in a convenient and reasonably rapid manner.

Miss Descoeudres chose nine tests as a measure of the power of speech. (8)

1. Naming opposites in pictures and objects shown.
2. Filling in missing words in ten easy omissions.
3. Repetition of numbers pronounced to child.
4. Naming six callings in response to such questions as, "who makes shoes?"
5. Naming six materials such as, "what are pencils made of."
6. Naming eight opposites from memory. "If your meat is not warm then it is . . . . . . ?"
7. Naming ten colors.
8. Finding twelve verbs, representing actions performed by the examiner or in which the child imitates action.
9. Giving a list of twenty-five words of increasing difficulty and finding out by question whether or not the child knows the meanings of the words.

To solve the exercises would require 103 correct answers.

The author gives norms based upon the study of some 300 Geneva children ranging in age from two and a half to seven years, from families of both working classes and educated classes.

When once the speech defect has been diagnosed, it

is possible to apply corrective measures, to graph the results from week to week, and to stimulate the child to improve his own record. There was also a need of a series of measurements for testing the child who could not read, the blind, the mentally defective and the deaf child. A picture test was first devised, covering some 100 English sounds, giving each consonant sound in initial, middle and final position. Later an object test was devised, the materials selected representing all the consonant and vowel sounds as listed in the International Phonetic Association alphabet.

The picture charts and the object test can be used with children who cannot read and are so arranged as to elicit the proper responses in the forms of names of familiar objects. They are therefore useful with the normal pre-school and the kindergarten child. Probably it is unwise to use a test involving reading in grades below the fourth. It was found that among first, second and third grade children in the Madison Public Schools, (Wisconsin), about 75% of the children tested made a satisfactory score when the picture-articulation test was used. The use of articulation tests in sentence form is therefore not advised below the fourth grade and the graded tests were arranged with this in mind.

The tests were undertaken not merely to enable the examiner to detect the type of speech defect, but to enable her to make a personality rating as well. After trying out a large number of tests such as substitution tests, memory for digits, word memory, language scales of various types, reading and vocabulary tests, a team of seven tests was chosen for standardization from those who gave the highest correlation coefficients, when compared with a standard.

The Blanton-Stinchfield (3) Speech Measurements are arranged in two parts. Part I. is subjective and provides for personality ratings, off-hand estimates by the examiner of the child's vocal quality, pitch, time elements (if fast or slow), enunciation, behavior characteristics, special handicaps or special abilities.

It includes a seven-point scale, each characteristic being rated on a basis of 1 to 3, (poor, average, superior). This gives a maximum rating of 21 points, a minimum of 7 points for a normal child and a possible zero for mentally deficient children.

The subjective judgment, when correlated with definite objective measurements such as oral reading, silent reading, vocabulary and spontaneous speech shows sufficiently high coefficients of correlation to warrant the inclusion in a series of objective measurements, of those tests which seem to be important in speech diagnosis.

Part II consists of a series of objective measurements, in a team of seven tests. (1) Articulation Test A, (containing all the sounds in English arranged in initial, middle, final position for consonants, and including also the word sounds) (2) Articulation Test B, (containing many of the commoner consonant combinations), (3) Oral Reading Rate, (4) Silent Reading Rate, (5) Spontaneous Speech Rate, (6) Percentage of Relevant Words used in Spontaneous Speech, and (7) Vocabulary.

The tests were given to all the children in each of eight grades in the Madison, Wisconsin public schools, to 150 University students at the University of Wisconsin, and to unselected groups of children in Chicopee and Springfield, Massachusetts. The adult (college level) test has been given to 1648 Freshman girls at Mount Holyoke College in 1922-27. The general value of the test is strikingly indicated by the fact that although 60-67% passed the test each year for 4 years, so that they were placed in the regular speech classes or in the excused group, one sixth failed to pass the test and one sixth were rated as belonging to the *superior group*. This gives a good curve of distribution, when compared with various psychological ratings of other types.

The tests show that a number of college girls held for speech training made low scores in oral and silent reading rate. Adults usually read silently at the rate of about four words per second. These tests show that the college girl reads slightly faster, or at a rate of between 4.9 words per second and 5.3 words per second, this being the median for the entire Freshman classes of 1919 and 1920.

The following table shows the average of *class medians* for four years, 1922-25 in the various tests, the testing material being that arranged for college students (4).

Medians.

Articulation test, A, 97 sounds in 100 correct.
Oral Reading rate, 170-190 words per minute.
Silent Reading rate, 220-300 words per minute.
Vocabulary, 75 words (in 100) defined. (Whipple Vocabulary test.)
Spontaneous speech rate, 120-140 words per minute.
Percentage of relevant words, 96%.

Table III shows the standing of 41 students in the special corrective group when compared with 41 unselected students from the superior speech group, on the basis of the tests given in the fall of 1926.

Table III.

Rating in Speech Measurements and in tests for Musical
Talent.

No. of students, Corrective group 41

No. of students, Superior group, 41, Total 82

Median Scores.

	Special Group	Superior Group
Speech index in subjective measurements,	14	17
Speech index in objective measurements,	13	15
Articulation Test A	93	97
Articulation Test B	93	98
Oral Reading (Wds. per minute)	184	180
Silent Reading (Wds. per minute)	274	294
Spontaneous Speech Rate	120	132
Percent. relevant words in spont. sp.	95%	96%
Vocabulary	74	72
Median average	106.6	111.0
Scores on Seashore Musical Tests.*	C—	C

SUMMARY.

(College girls.)

1.　The off-hand estimate of the speech performance of the
girl free from speech handicap is higher than the estimate made
of the girl who is placed in the speech correction group.

2.　The objective performance of the superior speech group
is higher than that of the special corrective group in such performances as in Articulation, in Silent and Oral Reading Rate,
and in percentage of Relevant Words used in Spontaneous
Speech.

3.　Sense of pitch, sense of intensity and tonal memory as

*The highest score made by any student in either group on the
Musical Tests was B, altho some higher scores were made in the
class as a whole.

Norms for the series of graded speech tests have been published
elsewhere. See Speech Measurements, Manual, Blanton-Stinchfield; C.
H. Stoelting Co., 424 No. Homan Ave., Chicago, Illinois.

shown by the Seashore Musical Ability Tests, enter into the function of speech. The score for the corrective group is lower than that for the superior group. These factors should therefore be considered in applying remedial speech measures.

4. The findings indicate that speech, intelligence, scholarship, auditory discrimination, and personality factors may be related, but they are not necessarily in a "causal sequence". On the whole, the person of higher intelligence seems more stable emotionally and makes a better adjustment in college life than does the less intelligent student.

5. The scholastic attainment of the special group is inferior to that of the superior speech group at the time of entrance to college. The scholastic attainment of the special corrective group remains inferior to that of the superior speech group at the end of the first year of college life.

6. On the basis of general intelligence, whatever it may include, the two groups are about equal as shown by the Scholastic Aptitude Tests and other intelligence tests given for the past five years to all entering students.

7. There is very little difference in the two groups on the basis of reports sent to the college by parents, principals and others at the time when application to college is made. After college entrance however, the students in the corrective group are found to be less easily adjusted than are the superior students. They are also more subject to personality disturbances, low scholarship, and other forms of maladjustment than are the girls classified in the superior speech group.

8. A larger number of girls in the special corrective group come from public schools than from private schools. The girls from private schools seem to pass the tests more easily. This indicates that private schools place a greater emphasis upon such factors as personality development, clearness of thought and expression. These girls from private schools perhaps come from homes where more emphasis is placed upon personality, speech, posture, and expressional activities generally. Miss Descoeudres in Germany found a similar difference between

two classes of children ranging in age from two and a half years to seven and a half years in tests involving "power of speech," and representing children from parents of the laboring class and children of educated parents.

9. A study of official records in the Department of Physical Education, Dean's Office, Board of Admissions and Department of Health shows that there is little difference in the physical comparison of the two groups. Both seem to be in equally good physical condition at time of college entrance. The special group shows a somewhat greater tendency to certain respiratory diseases such as frequent colds, influenza and tonsilitis, while a larger number in the superior group have had tonsils and adenoids removed. This seems to indicate a better mouth, nose and throat hygiene on the part of girls in the superior group. Both groups show an equal amount of susceptibility to the common diseases of childhood, according to past medical records. There is nothing on record in any instance at the time of college entrance in regard to speech or personality peculiarities among the girls examined for the past five years. Families and principals have ignored these peculiarities even when they should have been recognized as hindering a girl in making her economic and social adjustments in later life. Provision for notations in regard to speech and personality should be included as a part of the college entrance blanks, if students are to receive special attention in helping them to eliminate the difficulty during college years. Neglected, it may be in a large measure responsible for economic and social maladjustments at various points in one's career.

Table IV.

Distribution table showing results of speech tests both at Perkins Institution, Watertown, Mass. and at Pennsylvania Institution for the Instruction of the Blind, Overbrook, Pa. 1924-26.

	Upper School Girls	Boys	Kinder-garten Girls	Boys	Lower School Girls	Boys	Total Cases
vocal defect; harsh, etc...........	6	7		2	4		19
vocal defect; hoarse..............	1	1					2
Stutter, hesitation................	1	3	3	3		1	11
Letter substitution, with or without lisp...........................	2	4	8	9	4	2	29
Nasality.........................	3						3
Oral inaccuracy and letter substitution.........................	11	5	5	2	5	2	30
Jaw tension while speaking........	3	2					5
Mild oral inaccuracy..............	11	9	5	6	10	7	46
Foreign accent...................	1	1	1				3
Oral inaccuracy and lisp...........	12	3	5	1	1	1	23
Deafness with oral inaccuracy......	2	1	1			1	5
Lateral lisp......................					1		1
Cleft palate speech...............		1					1
Breathy quality or poor vocal quality					2		2
Emotional uncontrol..............					1	1	2
Nervousness, personality difficulty or psychotic tendency.............	6	4					10
Dementia Praecox quality of voice..				2			2
Negatively suggestible personality...	1						1
Monotonous, repressed, subdued tones...........................		1					1
Aphasia.........................						1	1
Paraphasia......................						1	1
Introvert, shut-in type (noticeably so)	1						1
Totals with speech defects........	61	42	30	23	28	17	201

Girls, 119
Boys, 82

SUMMARY.

Total numbers examined.   Upper school Girls 135, Boys 93
Kindergarten Girls 49, Boys 55
Lower School Girls 30, Boys 42

Total number examined 404

In the speech defect group there were, Boys 41%, Girls 59%, a total of 201 cases. 49% of the total number examined had speech difficulties ranging from mild letter substitutions and inaccuracies to stuttering, lisping, etc. The ratio of speech defects in the public school population is given by Wallin and others as 3 boys to 1 girl. It is interesting to note that in the schools for the blind, we find a larger number of girls having speech defects, the ratio being 3 girls to 2 boys.

In the elementary schools of Madison, Wisconsin for eight grades and university students tested, the percentage of speech defects, ranging from mild to severe was found to be 18% of the total number tested. It will be seen that the percentage in schools for the blind, is much larger. Among the significant tendencies found in the schools for the blind, were the following:

I.   Large number of letter substitution cases, 29 or 14%. Commonest among kindergarten children.

II.   Mild oral inaccuracy and lisping, 23 or 11%. Commonest among upper school girls.

III. Stutter or hesitant speech; broken rhythm, etc. 11 or 5%. Most common in the kindergarten.

MASTERING the technique of various related speech activities through the audito-visual, audito-motor and visuo-motor associations is a much more complicated process than is generally recognized, because we take so much for granted in regard to the learning process, that we fail to realize what a task faces the infant of today in acquiring a vocabulary. Primitive man might remain content with the development of a sign language, gestures and depictive forms of expression, but modern children if they are to compete successfully with other children in the environment must acquire during the first six years the ability to read, to write, to make themselves understood, to memorize a vast number of names of objects, to form associations for an immense number of objects, persons and things, and learn to articulate the names of these social "implements."

The aim of the acquisition of language is to perfect the process of communication through oral and written speech. From the standpoint of pedagogy, language study covers many activities; reading, silent and oral, spelling, writing, grammar and speech composition, written composition, and various forms of literary and artistic production.

It is surprising to many people to learn that there are a good many children of pre-school age who fail in this socialization process and some who do not learn to read during the entire first year in school. There are others whose speech becomes so conditioned by fear that they break down into habits of stuttering, or speak in jerky, unrhythmic sentences. They may fail to overcome these habits just as they fail to overcome other types of handicaps unless remedial measures are applied. A surprising number of school children lisp. A small number stutter. Various investigators have found that the incidence of speech defects when boys and girls are compared, is in the ratio of three boys to one girl. It is generally agreed that at the outset girls are rather more facile than boys in the mastering of language. It is often quite impossible to eradicate inaccuracies of speech found in adult life. It is comparatively easy to remedy them if recognized and dealt with in the early formative years in school and home.

Diagnostic language scales in use in public schools show that whatever the language ability measured, it increases with age and grade. How much is due to training and how much to native ability, linguistic skill and environment, it is difficult to say. Trabue found a .83 coefficient of correlation between the Binet Test mental age scale and his own language scale. The Army Alpha test shows a correlation of $+70$ between intelligence grades and English. In the matter of speech composition, training in grammatical construction, syntax, punctuation, spelling and the like, proficiency seems to be more a matter of habit, due to training and usage, than a native ability. We know that drill and intensive training often overcome defects and deficiencies in handicapped children. On the other hand, some children who are specially gifted in certain fields may be seriously handicapped by the lack of early training in spelling, punctuation, reading and writing.*

The superiority of girls over boys in language ability is evident also from the language scales, as it has been shown that girls write longer and better compositions than do boys. Speech surveys show that girls have fewer speech handicaps, and that generally they are slightly more precocious in language development than are boys.

The same principles which apply to the improvement of oral and written language apply to the elimination of speech defects. Here we have one of the most recent developments in the field of special subjects. In the up-to-date school today there is some provision for every handicapped child, whether due to defective vision, defective hearing, or because he is crippled. Special classes for mentally deficient children are a part of many school systems and we have even established classes for the precocious child, that he may not be held to the average attainment of the majority of the children of his age level. It is in the newer realm of special handicaps involving speech disability that greater attention must be given by educators to drill and special classes. Speech correction is included

*Reed. The Psychology of Elementary School Subjects. Ginn & Co., Boston, 1927, Pp. 273-283.

in the curricula of schools in some cities such as Detroit, where at least thirty-two teachers of the subject are employed, with centers in all of the larger school districts. Boston, Madison (Wisconsin), Los Angeles, San Francisco, New York, Philadelphia, St. Louis, Pittsburgh, Harrisburg, Grand Rapids, and Minneapolis give attention to this work through the establishment of a special department or by special teachers exclusively engaged in speech correction work.

In a speech survey made in St. Louis in 1915-16 including 98,057 children, it was found that 2.8% were speech defectives.*

Conradi (10) made a school survey in 1904 in several American cities including 87,440 children, and found that 2.46% were speech defect cases. Dr. Smiley Blanton in a survey of Madison Schools including 8,000 cases in seventeen schools found the incidence of speech defects to be 5.6%. Miss Pauline Camp found 13% in the schools of Grand Rapids. She attributes this larger number to the fact that she personally examined each child included in the survey, whereas most of the surveys previously made had been based upon questionnaire methods and reports made by teachers untrained in the field of speech defects.

In 1922 the writer, giving speech tests to all children in each of eight grades in the Madison, Wisconsin public schools found 18% having speech difficulties ranging from relatively mild to severe. In six years of speech testing at Mount Holyoke College, including all the entering students in classes from the fall of 1922 to 1927 an average of 16% of the class each year has been classified in the speech correction group because of difficulties from mild to severe.

*Report of Board of Education, St. Louis, Mo., J. E. Wallin.

Grouping by means of the Speech Tests at Mount Holyoke College, for four years (1922-25) on the old basis and 1926-27 on new basis.

Total number 1678.

TABLE I.

Showing percent of students in each speech group,

Years 1922-25, when some students were excused.

Group.	1922	1923	1924	1925	Total, 1922-25.
I.	18%	16%	16%	16%	(Aver.) 16%
II.	19%	24%	44%	29%	" 30%
III.	35%	42%	29%	41%	' 37%
IV.	28%	18%	11%	14%	·· 17%
Total,	100%	100%	100%	100%	100%

Key to Grouping in above table.

> Group I. Required Freshman Corrective work (Psychol. Dept.)
>
> Group II. Required Sophomore speech classes (Speech Dept.)
>
> Group III. Satisfactory; excused from speech requirement.
>
> Group IV. Superior. Advised to elect while in college.

TABLE II.   Showing percent of students in each group when all students are held for some requirement, except those with advanced standing in speech from other colleges. 1926-27.

	1926-1927	Aver.		*Key to grouping.*
Group I.	19%	11%	15%	Group I. Corrective work.
Group II.	28%	46%	37%	Group II. Required Freshman speech classes.
Group III.	48%	40%	44%	Group III. May elect in any of upperclass years.
Group IV.	5%	3%	4%	Group IV. Advanced standing in speech from other colleges.
Total	100%	100%	100%	

TABLE III.   Frequency table showing types of speech difficulty for which students have been held in Group I. Years
1922-25.

Oral inaccuracy and ineffective speech, ... 35%
Vocal peculiarity, hoarse, harsh, nasal, etc. 21%
Lisping 16%
Stutter, nervous hesitancy or speechblocking 11%
Foreign accent, ... 6%
Letter substitution, ... 5%
Provincial dialect, ... 3%
Deafness and oral inaccuracy due to same, ... 2%
Paralysis (associated with ineffective speech) 1%

Total, ...100%

Percentage is that of total number in *group I, not percentage*
of entire Freshman class.

In one first grade tested by the writer the supervisor
of kindergarten activities and a number of her teachers had taken a special course in Speech Correction
and Child Psychology, and had secured appreciable
results in clearing up difficulties such as lisping, oral
inaccuracies and foreign accent, in a relatively short
period of time.

Foreign accent is not usually considered as a "speech
defect", but it is within the province of the grade
teacher to eliminate it, and she should also *attempt* to
secure clear-cut incisive enunciation from all of the
children in her grade. In the Polish language, where
the *th* (voiced and voiceless) is usually displaced by a
d or *t* sound, some knowledge of phonetics is necessary that the teacher may show the child how to make
the proper contacts in order to give the *th* sound,
which is a lingua-dental, instead of the *t* or *d* sounds,
which are lingua-rugal. The Polish child also gives

a *g* in addition to the *ng* sound in such words as *ringing,* and *going,* ("ring-ging" for *ringing;* going-g for *going*). Letter substitutions and minor inaccuracies of this type may be easily corrected in the first grades in school. A few moments a day, given by either special teacher or class room teacher to phonetic exercises, word and sentence drill, including the difficult sounds for the particular group of children dealt with are sufficient to aid children to replace undesirable speech habits by desirable speech standards.

The normal schools and colleges of this country should include speech correction and special courses in the psychology of language development as a part of the teacher-training requirement. This is done in many foreign countries. Early in the century Belgium, Germany, Switzerland and Denmark established special schools or special classes for the speech defective, with specially trained teachers to conduct this work.

Where defects exist in addition to those of speech, there seems to be a higher percentage of speech defects than we find among non-handicapped children. In a speech survey of the two largest state schools for the Blind, namely the Perkins Institution for the Instruction of the Blind at Watertown, Massachusetts and the Pennsylvania Institution for the Instruction of the Blind, at Overbrook, Pennsylvania, 48% of the total number tested could be properly classified in the speech defect group. The girls were in the majority, on account of the large number of cases of lisping among them. There were 59% girls and 41% boys in the total 100% (of those having speech defects) a ratio of 3 girls to 2 boys. Blindness seems to favor the hangover of infantile speech habits slightly longer among girls than among boys. In both, we find poorer

habits of posture, more passivity of the muscles of expression, less vital capacity and poorer habits of
speech generally than in the public school population
tested. It will be recalled that the ratio of speech defects is greater among boys than among the girls in
the public school population.

Table IV summarizes the results of the speech surveys given in the Watertown and Philadelphia schools
for the blind, 1923-25.*

Total No. examined.

		Lower		Upper		Total	
Kindergarten,		school,		school,		all schools.	
Girls	49	Girls	30	Girls	135	Girls	214
Boys	55	Boys	42	Boys	93	Boys	190
				Total No. Examined		404.	

Total No. with speech defects.

Girls	30	Girls	28	Girls	61	Girls	119
Boys	23	Boys	17	Boys	42	Boys	82
				No. with Speech defects		201	

Speech is held to be one of the most recently acquired of the highly skilled performances of man, in
his evolution from the lower to the higher type of
nervous system. It is also one of the first skilled performances to show deterioration in instances where
the mental development is below normal, or where
disintegration of personality has taken place as among
the insane. Studies of the speech of the insane furnishes
a rich field for those interested in the study of the disintegration of mental processes. In manic depressive
insanity when the manic phase predominates, one often
finds a high "speech pressure", the individual talking

*Stinchfield, S. M. Speech Defects in Children. Amer. Associa. of
Instructors of the Blind. 28th Bien. Convention, Proc., 1926, pp.
301-306.

incessantly for days or hours at a time. It is the quality of the speech reaction at this time which gives the psychiatrist important cues as to the cause of the disturbance, or to certain exciting causes which have become manifest in the symptom of speech pressure and excessive volubility.

Despite these high frequencies for speech defects in specially handicapped children, both teachers and the school psychologists state that the speech has improved a great deal since these children entered the state institutions. This holds both for the mentally deficient children and for those in the two schools for the blind. This improvement is attributed to the improvement in environmental conditions, improved hygiene, food, rest, recreation, and training. It is a part of the socialization process.

If speech training has thus been found to be effective among specially handicapped children, rendering them more efficient workers and yielding returns in increased happiness and satisfaction, then it is obvious that the public schools should do all in their power to remove the special handicap of a speech defect in the children committed to their care, in order to overcome this remedial handicap during the early formative years. The importance of this training has been sufficiently well stated and emphasized elsewhere, in books dealing with the handicapped child.

How may we call it to the attention of American educators in order that they may consider it in its economic and social aspects? How should we train a child suffering from any special handicap? There are several possibilities.

First: Educators should be aware of the fact that speech defects are on the increase in the civilian population, due to the influx of many languages, varying social standards within the same language group, increase in nervous disorders, complexities in modern community life, and the greater nervous strain of the present day upon the child. We should seek agencies for the correction of these difficulties.

Secondly: It should be possible for the child with a speech difficulty to receive special and individual attention; otherwise he cannot progress at the usual rate in a mixed class of 20 or more children in the ordinary school room.

Third: A special case history study should be made, including medical and family history, social history, school progress, home environment, economic status, the psychobiological factors mentioned by Blanton and others in dealing with speech defectives,—character and temperament, interests and ambitions, nature of speech defect, diagnosis, prognosis, treatment and results. (5)

Fourth: A speech hygiene program should be given to each child and its parents, in order that the home may cooperate with the school in overcoming the speech difficulty.*

Fifth: Daily drill and speech exercises should be given to the child alone, or in small groups of children with the same handicap. Children with different defects need different treatment and should not be dealt with together.

Sixth: The personality of the teacher is an important element in effecting a cure. It is therefore important that normal schools should secure specially trained teachers to carry on this important branch of special service for the speech-handicapped child.

*See Speech Hygiene Program.

Seventh: Cooperation between various agencies and institutions is necessary to secure maximum efficiency, as has been shown by the work done in countries where a central institute has been established to deal with speech defect cases, or where all the work in a group of cities has been carried on under national or local educational supervision and where the training is a part of the recognized educational procedure. Reliable institutions do not usually *"guarantee"* cures to stutterers or others, nor do they employ unscientific, haphazard methods, exacting a disproportionate fee for services rendered.

Eighth: It is known to physicians and laymen that a child possessing a physical handicap which is allowed to go uncorrected, usually cannot compete mentally or physically with a normal, robust child of good physique. It is the exception rather than the rule, for speech-defect cases to excel mentally or physically. The child with a speech difficulty tends to become morbid, introspective, suspicious, unsocial and even psychotic in his personality reactions. This decreases his efficiency as well as his economic value to the community.

Speech Hygiene Program, For Daily Practise.*

I. Regular hours of sleep, nine hours or more per night. Retire at 8.30, if you are less than eighteen years old,—an hour later, as a customary thing, if you are older.

II. Try to go to sleep directly, with pleasant, cheerful thoughts. The easiest way to accomplish this, is to relax completely as possible, and to seek to become "drowsy."

*All of the above directions apply to practically all speech students, but numbers 13 and 14 are intended particularly for those who stutter.

III. Try not to become very much excited when you are talking. Cultivate habits of calm, easy speech, free from hesitation, "noises" and nervous mannerisms.

IV. Say to yourself, "I am not afraid; I know that I can make all the sounds in the English language. I will try to speak them easily and well."

V. Use pleasant, agreeable tones. Try to get out of a jerky, unrhythmic monotone in speech, if such is your usual way of speaking.

VI. Eat plenty of fruits and green, leafy vegetables when you can secure them. Avoid eating sweets to excess. Do not spend your allowance for candy.

VII. Eat slowly and masticate your food thoroughly.

VIII. Exercise each day out of doors for at least two hours.

IX. Keep a cheerful, pleasant attitude all the time.

X. Don't worry about your speech. It is worry which sends it off into a jerky, unpleasant utterance. Calmness and control of yourself, whenever you begin to speak, will give you easy, fluent utterance if you practise it often enough.

XI. Remember that it will take time to improve, but begin NOW to relax and make up your mind that you are going to conquer your speech habits rather than let them master YOU!

XII. Read "The Americanization of Edward W. Bok", and like him seek every possible occasion to improve yourself, to talk with interesting people, to take some of the social responsibility of each occasion upon yourself, and thus direct the development of your own personality.

XIII. Remember that an occasional hesitation is to be expected for some time, if you have stuttered for a good many years,—but *stop* the moment hesitation or jerky speech occurs and get a new grip on yourself; make a new and better start, without facial contortions, grimaces and "tied-up" muscle movements of head and shoulders. Be a self-starter, of the mental type; don't let your hands and feet start the performance!

XIV. Relax, relax, RELAX! Speech should be easy and spontaneous. Call some of your friends on the telephone occasionally, or answer the calls whenever possible, until you can do this successfully. Boys and girls who stutter often have a strange fear of the telephone. Overcome this fear, realizing that it is easier to talk to some people over the telephone, than in the same room.

XV. Do not depend on some other member of your family to talk for you, thus assuming the social responsibility which should be partly yours. Be gracious and tactful enough to do your share, and try to do it easily and well. Self-consciousness is the bug-bear which most often makes us feel awkward and appear ill-at-ease.

Speech Hygiene Program For the Family.

I. Fathers and Mothers, — cultivate calm easy speech in your homes, and desire it also from every member of your family. Avoid nervous haste, hurry and excitement in talking. Seek to be reasonably deliberate in speech and to serve as a constant model of natural, gracious, easy speech, to your sons and daughters.

II. Quietly suggest that each child talk slowly and clearly at home.

III. Encourage the child to talk,—find things of interest for him to talk about, but insist upon good speech from the very start.

IV. Distinctness of utterance, careful manners, quiet, self-assured speech is to be held up to the child as an ear-mark of good breeding.

V. Insist upon good manners in little things, as the child passes out of the five year old period,—teaching children to wait upon you, to pull your chair or that of guests at the table, to allow you to precede, in entering a room; show him that you want him to do himself and the family credit, in a social way, both at home and abroad.

VI. If a child hesitates or blocks off in speech, or tries to talk too rapidly, stop him *quietly,* and ask him to begin again. Have him stop AT ONCE; do not let the stutter habit gain a foothold, if you can help it. Do not let him speak on an incoming breath; he should breathe in slowly and then speak on the outgoing breath.

VII. Help the child to overcome the "stoop-shoulder" habit. Cultivate erect bearing, obey the Posture Rules like good soldiers. Remember that we should carry the head erect, chest expanded, knees straight (not sagging in indolent fashion)—and hips well back. Do not let child sit for hours curled up in a chair, bending over a book. He can sit well if required to do so.

VIII. Help children to cultivate calm, cheerful dispositions, free from whining, nervousness, worry or mental strain.

IX. Practise bodily exercises and simple gymnastics each day.

1. Arm stretching exercises.

2. Head rotations, bending and flexions.

3. Freedom of shoulders (in arm movements).

4. Breathing exercises (without directing attention to the ACT of breathing or the muscles concerned!) Get at it indirectly through counting, phrasing, sentence building, etc. Work for smooth, easy responses, counting in groups of numbers, five counts on one breath. In this manner, count from 1 to 5, then 5-10; —10-15;—15-20; and 20 to 25.

Count to 50 in groups of 10 (10 to each breath).

Count to 45 in groups of 15.

Say the alphabet on one breath.

Read some short poem, being sure that you take a new breath for each line. If this is too difficult, take a new breath for each phrase, speaking slowly and distinctly.

Articulation Test.

On following pages are given 34 sentences, each containing three sounds to be checked or credited, with the exception of the last sentence which contains only one sound to be checked. The score is 100: or 33 times 3 plus 1 (for the final sentence) Total 100 points.

Score yourself or ask observer to check you, using the accompanying check sheet for same. The sentences here given contain all the Sounds of English as listed in the International Phonetic Association alphabet, with a few additional consonant combinations, making a total of 100 possible points. See footnote for information regarding additional testing material.*

*Used by courtesy of C. H. Stoelting & Co., Chicago, Ill., publishers of Blanton-Stinchfield Speech Measurements, Graded Series, Grades I-VIII, and Adult Tests.

Sentences.	Test sounds.		
1. He could not adhere to the whig plan.	h	h	wh
2. He fell, baffled off the cliff.	f	f	f
3. You have a good view of the river, from the cove.	v	v	v
4. Can you bring the basket at eight o'clock?	k	k	k
5. The girl was dragging a heavy bag of potatoes.	g	g	g
6. The monk was ringing the gong.	nk	ng	ng
7. Pick the apples when they are ripe.	p	p	p
8. He brought the rubber ball for Rob.	b	b	b
9. The mob heard the rumbling of the drum.	m	m	m
10. Try to bail the water out of the boat.	t	t	t
11. I did not wonder at the deed.	d	d	d
12. He brought us some nuts and a candy cane.	n	n	n
13. The child was scratching a match on the chair.	ch	ch	ch
14. Jack put the toy engine on the bridge.	j	j	j
15. She was washing that dish.	sh	sh	sh
16. The tape measure is brown and gilt.	br	zh	lt
17. I saw the basket of lace.	s	s	s
18. Zero is called the freezing point.	z	z	z
19. Walter was away last Christmas.	w	w	kr
20. Have you read the news about the flight?	y	ew	fl
21. This is the leather with the smooth finish.	th	th	th
22. I think the author's name is Smith.	th	th	th
23. The ladder was taken from building to the wall.	l	l	l
24. Right near the tree it stands.	r	(t)r	-ear
25. Over there is a flower.	ou	-ere	ow
26. He could see that the apple was bitten.	ēē	ă	ĭ
27. He came and brought the wire for our radio.	ā	-ire	our
28. The bird hovered over the water.	ə:(ir)	(hover)	aw
29. The poor child was looking for a star in the book.	-oor	a:	o͝o
30. The boy did not come soon enough.	oi	ŏ	o͞o

31. I can see the squirrel, scrambling and scolding.	škw	sk	skr	
32. The fly alighted near the cup.	ī	ŭ	-ear	
33. Hugo met with a troublesome fate.	h̊y	ĕ		tr
34. Give me the glasses, please.	gl			

References.

1. ANDERSON, LEWIS. *A Preliminary Report of an Experimental Analysis of Causes of Stuttering.* Jour. of Appl. Psychol., Dec., 1921.
2. BALDWIN-STECHER. *The Psychology of the Pre-School Child.*
3. BLANTON-STINCHFIELD. *Speech Measurements, Speech Manual.* C. H. Stoelting & Co., Chicago, Illinois, 1923.
4. DOWNEY, J. *Will Temperament and Its Testing.* World Book Co., 1923.
5. GRAY, S. J. *Public Speaking Test,* 1928, Expression Co., Boston.
6. ROBBINS. *A Plethysmographic Study of Shock and Stammering.* Amer. Jour. of Physiology. Vo. 48, No. 3, Apr., 1919.
7. SEASHORE. *Tests for Musical Ability.* Columbia Phonograph Co., N. Y.
8. STERN. *The Psychology of Early Childhood.* Pp. 174-178. Tests and measurements of speech.
9. STINCHFIELD. *The Formulation and Standardization of a Series of Graded Speech Exercises.* Psychol. Rev. Monograph Series.
10. STINCHFIELD. *Some Relationships between Speech Defects, Musical Disability, Scholastic Attainment and Maladjustment.* Quarterly Journal of Speech Education, June, 1927.
11. TRAVIS. *The relation between faulty speech and Lack of Certain Musical Talents.* Psychol. Monog. Vol. XXXVI:10.
12. TOWN. *Analytic Study of a Group of Five and Six Year Old Children.* Iowa Child Welfare Station Monograph Series, May, 1921. Pp. 31-33.

Chapter VI

EXERCISES FOR THE TREATMENT OF STUTTERING, LISPING, NA-SALITY, CLEFT-PALATE SPEECH AND THAT OF THE DEAF

I. *Stuttering.*

PHONETIC methods should be employed for cases other than stuttering. In dealing with stutterers it is preferable to work upon words, phrases, sentences, spontaneous speech, through playing store, imaginary conversations applying for a position, dialogue, simple dramatizations, short stories, humorous incidents and social responses of similar type. Intense drill in phonics and phonetic training has been held by some physicians to be responsible for an increase in stuttering, after such a system was installed in the school.

Stuttering is generally closely related to the perceptual processes and motor activities. The child tends to respond positively and immediately to incoming stimuli. His choice reactions are less discriminating than those of adults. It is easy therefore to over-stimulate him, and parents often do not understand that the child's nervous system cannot endure an over amount of stimulation without becoming more easily exhausted than is the case with the adult. In reading we tend to reduce motor movements to a minimum. In speaking we find that the motor speech mechanism often cannot keep pace with the thinking or with the eye movements,

In *Silent Reading* we know that there are means of measuring the eye-voice span, to see how much the eye takes in beyond the words which are being spoken. In stuttering there seems to be a delay in the transmission of the motor speech impulse to the peripheral speech musculature. It has been shown by Travis in experiments at Iowa that there is a central blocking or delay in the rate of nerve impulse in stutterers and left-handed children. When there is no blocking or central inhibition, the speech response is immediate and spontaneous and seems like a single simple response. But a blocking may occur at any one of a number of places.

Shallow breathing, incorrect posture, laryngeal, respiratory or diaphragmatic cramps, or a combination of these, are apparent in many stutterers, but by calling attention to these one may interfere with freedom of movement and retard corrective work. With the stutterer it is important to work by indirection, more than with any other type of speech defect, whereas with most speech difficulties, such as lisping or letter substitution, phonetic training and letter position may be safely taught. This is based upon the findings of Blanton, and is in accordance with psychiatric principles laid down by mental hygienists. The same treatment is applied to all cases, regardless, by many of the older systems of speech reëducation, but this is a dangerous practise, because the stutterer is already hesitating on initial consonants or repeating them at the end of his words. Why risk intensifying the difficulty by centering attention on these elements, when the vowel sound is the chief tonal element in the word? The vowel gives no difficulty unless in an initial position. Even then it occasions less blocking than do the consonants. Working for rounded, rich, full vowel tones rather than upon specific letters may be helpful, but the word or phrase is more important than directing attention to any one element in the word.

If shown by means of a speech test that he is able to make the various sounds correctly in certain words, he may gradually be led to an understanding of the psychic element involved in his occasional blocking upon certain sounds. Once knowing that he can make these sounds he is able to do it more frequently, as he understands there is nothing abnormal about his vocal apparatus.

II. *Exercises to Aid in Overcoming Stuttering.*

A.   Directions—(to teacher who reads aloud with pupil.)

"Read with me the following lines. Try to think of yourself as Patrick Henry addressing the Continental Congress, and say"—

"What is it that gentlemen wish? What would they have? Shall we try argument? Shall we resort to force and entreaty? Sir, we shall *not* fail!"

B.   Directions—(teacher.)

"Read the following aloud with me"—

'While he from forth the closet brought a heap
Of candied apple, quince, and plum, and gourd;
With jellies smoother than the creamy curd,
And lucent syrups, tinct with cinnamon;
Manna and dates, in argosy transferr'd
From Fez; and spiced dainties, every one,
From silken Samarcand to cedar's Lebanon.'

C.   Directions—(teacher.)

"Read the following aloud with me";

'The desire of the moth for the star,
   Of the night for the morrow,
The devotion to something afar
   From this sphere of our sorrow.

And the night shall be filled with music,
    And the cares that infest the day,
Shall fold up their tents, like the Arabs,
    And as silently steal away.

D. (Teacher begins reading the following selection with student, but occasionally stops and lets him carry on the words by himself.)
    If we mean to preserve inviolate those inestimable privileges for which we have been so long contending and which we have pledged ourselves never to abandon until the glorious object of our contest shall be obtained. WE MUST FIGHT!

E. (Same.) I saw him in Russia, where the infantry of the snow and the cavalry of the wild blast scattered his legions like winter's withered leaves. I saw him at Leipsic, in defeat and disaster, driven by a million bayonets back upon Paris,—clutched like a wild beast,—banished to Elba.

F. (Same). We know that this policy is unwise because it is effective, and so we plead that it be defeated.

G. The student should next read the above selections aloud, without any "starters" or aids from the teacher. Make a good "breath" preparation, see that you feel at ease, relaxed, calm and ready, and then begin.

H. Pretend that you are a brakeman at some junction, calling off railway stations, such as:—
    "New Haven: change here for Springfield, White River Junction, Hartford, Meriden, Greenfield and Montreal. Remain in this car for Providence, New York, Washington and stations south! Trains for Boston and the Shore Line leave in one hour!

I. Be a store keeper and answer my questions as I come to buy groceries (shoes, dress goods, auto supplies.)

J. Be a salesman and try to sell me an automobile, or a book, or phonograph, some Xmas gifts, or embroidery.

K. Imagine yourself at the telephone, and call my number, inviting me to go to a concert, theatre or party.

L. Call the garage by telephone, and ask them to send a mechanic to repair your car, which is out of order.

M. Call the ticket agent at the railroad station and arrange for tickets and reservation from New York to Chicago over the Pennsylvania R. R. and Michigan Central lines.

N. Telephone to the theatre and reserve tickets for the next performance for a party of friends.

O. As I speak the following words, give the opposites, or the first opposite which comes in your mind:—

1. go (come).	7. failure
2. up	8. wise
3. father	9. pretty
4. sister	10. speak
5. happy	11. black
6. rise	12. open

P. Use each of the above words in turn, in a sentence.

Q. Using these illustrations, tell me the story the picture brings to your mind, connected with your own experience or some story you may have read. (Use pictures for stimulus here.)

R. Complete the following sentences:—
1. He decided to forget about the_____.
2. Will you walk with me to_____?
3. What did you do with the_____?
4. Where is the_____?
5. You can't afford to neglect your_____.

S. Use each of the following words in a sentence.

partner   dance   sharp   party
increase   play   win   book

happy	work	home	walk
merry	giggle	mother	boat
girl	honest	father	swim
serious	crayon	brother	whistle
sister	boy	sister	picture

T. Complete these sentences in more than one word:—

    1. His partner confessed to_____.

    2. The copper stock was sold at_____.

    3. The town was flooded by_____.

    4. They enticed the victim until_____.

    5. They entered the street car and_____.

    6. Early and late, he_____.

    7. He drove along the beach until he came to_____.

    8. On the left was a large____and on the right____.

    9. The clever animal performed_____.

    10. Do not begin anything unless you intend to_____.

U. Pronounce distinctly each of the following words and use each of them in a sentence:—

attention	prescribe	Manchester
concentration	aspirant	aggregation
recapitulation	celebrated	congregation
despicable	prestige	intervention
exemplary	opportune	substitution
nomination	extraordinary	constitution
recommendation	Worcester	prohibition

V. Answer these questions as rapidly as possible speaking clearly and distinctly:—

1. What is the difference between snatch and take?

2. " " " " " to feast and to devour?

3. " " " " " a lake and a river?

4. " " " " " a team and a wagon?

5. " " " " " misery and sadness?

6. " " " " mischief and evil?

7. " " " " " right and proper?

8. " " " " " ugly and awkward?

W. Find a short story in some book or magazine and tell it to me when you come tomorrow. Tell me a short story now, if you can think of one.

X. Think of some fable or fairy tale and tell it as if to a group of children.

Y. Retell some adventure of your own, or that of a friend.

Z. Discuss several of the following topics:—
   a. My favorite author.
   b. The ghost I thought I saw.
   c. The best play I ever saw.
   d. My favorite movie actor.
   e. Why I like football better than baseball.
   f. College spirit.
   g. School athletics.
   h. Missing a train.
   i. My summer vacation.
   j. What I like best of all to do.
   k. What I intend to do when I leave school.
   l. How to earn money in spare time.
   m. Automobiles.
   n. Trouble with a traffic officer.
   o. School days.
   p. The way to catch a trout.
   q. Where the boats come from (in New York Harbor.)
   r. Why I like to live in the East (or West).
   s. The best Indian story I ever read.
   t. Tell me the story of some adventure of your own.
   u. Tell me a short humorous story.

III. *Exercises For Home Practise.*

I.

READ first one part and then the other, with someone, in a dialogue.

THE WEATHER.

A. Do you mind this cold weather?

B. Not very much, though the thermometer hovers close to zero this morning.

A. It must be colder on your side of the street.

B. Yes, we are on the north side of the avenue.

A. Do you find it difficult to heat your house?

B. Not ordinarily, but on windy days the front of the house is very cold.

A. We never find cold even in severe weather.

B. You are indeed fortunate. Perhaps you have a better furnace than we.

A. Ours was installed last winter. We use an oil heater you know.

B. Is that so? We are using coal.

A. We are due for a severe storm.

B. Yes, the papers have predicted a cold wave.

A. It is very cold in the midwest.

B. It may not affect us, though.

A. Did you notice the moonlight on the snow last evening?

B. Yes, it was brilliant after the storm.

A. Are you going to Florida this year?

B. I want to, but my family prefers to stay at home this year.

A. That is too bad.

B. Yes, I enjoy a change of climate in winter.

II. Use these words in sentences. Speak slowly and clearly. Do not hurry.

material	ferocious	alligator	crocodile	elephant	zoo
Lindbergh	accuse	elementary	pulpit	oration	accurate
excavate	exaggerate	eliminate	expedition	north	pole
eraser	aviator	aviation	flying	sailing	mariner
practise	exercise	lesson	school	recite	pause
skilful	attentive	dreams	boys	girls	indifferent
memory	speak	slowly	carefully	try	work
think	listen	voices	singing	talking	saying

III. Practise with rising and falling inflections.

(Try to get an entire octave into your speaking voice

Ah,   ay,   ee,   Oh,   oo,
   ah;   ay;   ee;   oh; $\overline{co}$.

1,   3,   5,   7,   9,   11,   13,
  2;   4;   6;   8;   10;   12;   14.

Oh   oh   what   are   ah   see
   no;   yes;   ho;   no;   yes;   here.

Come   do   see   ah,   ay,   oo,
   now;   go;   here;   oh;   ee;   oh.

Exercises for Muscle Training and Speech Ability.

IV.

To secure clear-cut, distinct enunciation, we must be certain that the speech organs articulate correctly. The various agents must be able to take what ever position is necessary for the making of successive sounds. The above exercises should help you in cultivating incisive speech with precision and definiteness in use of the vocal organs.

A. Lips and Tongue. Extended position, try vowels, ah, ay, ee. Narrowed, rounded position. Try vowels aw, oh, oo. Try different combinations of same, as Ah, ah, ee; ee–ah–oo; oo, ee–ay; ay–ah–oh; aw–ee–oo. Voiced and voiceless sounds of consonants as follows: F–V; S–Z; Th–Th; T–D; P–B; K–G; Ch–J; Sh–Zh.

B. Larynx. Raise and lower, counting one to 10, raising pitch gradually as you count; ready! 1, 2, 3, 4, 5, 6, 7, 8, 9, 10.
Same lowering tone gradually as you come down from 10 to 1; 10, 9, 8, 7, 6, 5, 4, 3, 2, and 1.

Same with vowel sounds, raising tones on ah, ay, e, oh, oo, aw. Lower, on aw, oo, oh, e, ay, ah.

C. Uvula. Raise and lower on ah–ng–ah sounds.
ay–ung–ay; ee–ong–ee; oh–ong–oh; ōō–ung–ōō; hang–ay; hung–ee; hang–äh; hang–aye.

D. Breathing Exercises.*
1. Chest erect; breathe in slowly and out slowly.
2. Breathe in slowly and out rapidly on whispers.
3. Breathe in rapidly and out slowly on word *home—m–m.*
4. Breathe in as you count silently to 5; hold 5 counts and release breath in 5 counts.
5. Count to 20 in groups of 5; same to 10 in groups of 10; same to fifty in groups of 10; count to 25 on one breath. Repeat as much of the alphabet as you can on one breath.

(Keep good chest expansion, not moving up and down as you breathe.) Expand front, abdominal or lower costal muscles as you breathe in. Release as you breathe out.

V. *Articulation Exercises. S and Z Sounds.*

A. In normal speech the sound of s is articulated by placing the blade (or tip) of the tongue against the

Note: The breathing exercises should never be used with stutterers, since, as stated in the section referring to stuttering habits, the calling of attention in such cases to musculature involved in speech interferes with freedom and ease in coördination. However, they may be used in dealing with practically all other types of speech defects. There is always a certain danger in applying formal speech exercises, and the teacher needs special training and great power of discrimination in order to select such exercises as may be helpful or needful in individual cases. Some may recover precision in speech and freedom from stuttering merely by helpful analysis, knowledge of mental conflicts and suggestions for their solution.

ridge of the upper teeth, the front of the tongue being raised in the direction of the hard palate. The
teeth may be close together or slightly separated,
but the sound cannot be properly pronounced, with
the mouth wide open. Some speakers pronounce the
sound with the tip of the tongue lowered, but the
majority of speakers use the raised position (against
upper teeth).

Exercises for Practise.

sale	seem	sign	sew	soon
sane	seed	sight	sold	soothe
saint	seal	sigh	soap	soup
same	sea	shine	sow	superior
Seine	seek	side	sole	

1. He saw the gleaming cross beside the roadside.
2. At sight of the spectacle his resentment arose.
3. I saw the picture of Saint Cecelia in this chapel.
4. Have you seen the present which Santa Claus brought my sister?
5. It is absurd to use so much ink on this paper.
6. Please place the vase on the opposite side of the shelf.
7. This is the latest Atlas, I am certain.
8. The child stirred restlessly in his sleep.
9. If you insist, I shall be pleased to repeat the ghost story.
10. The ice is melting so rapidly that the skating is unsafe.
11. After a stormy session Saul listened to the songs.
12. The sounds of the zither resounded through the prison walls.
13. She saw the ship, a shining shape, upon a glimmering sea.
14. The falls of the Southland were rising and leaping as they tumbled over the sharp rocks.

   Z sounds. Z is a voiced consonant, corresponding to the voiceless or "whispered" sound of S.

B. Practise words:—

zone	zeal	Zion	Zulu	zounds

Zola	Zebra	Zest	scissors	zones
observe	reserves	please	dogs	pegs
trees	gives	dozen	busy	dissolve

1. Susan was resolved to see the Zebra at the zoo.
2. I have observed the cause of his complaints against the laws.
3. It gives her pleasure to do kind things for others.
4. Zola was an exile from France, because of political reasons.

C. Gems from President Coolidge:

Read the following with attention to all s and z sounds.

1. It may be of little importance to determine at any time just where we are, but it is of the utmost importance to determine where we are going.
2. Reverence is the measure not of the others, but of ourselves.
3. Men do not make laws. They do but discover them.
   Laws must be justified by something more than the will of the majority. They must rest on the eternal foundation of righteousness.
4. We need more of the office-desk and less of the show-window, in politics. Let men in office substitute the midnight oil for the lime-light.

D. Exercises for lisping or for indistinct S and Z sounds.

Exercise I. S – S – S – S   Z – Z – Z – Z
         Ss– Ss– Ss– S   Zz– Zz– Zz– Z
         Sss– Sss–Sss– S   Zzz– Zzz– Zzz– Z
         Ssss– Ssss– Ssss– S   Zzzz– Zzzz– Zzzz Z

Exercise II. Sah, say, see, saw, soh, soo.
             Zah, zay, zee, zaw, zoh, zoo.

Exercise III. Ay – say, ee –see, oh–sow, oo–soo.
              ay –zay,   ee–zee,   oh–zoh, OO–zoo.

Exercise IV. Word and sentence practise.

sardine	Zane	aside	ozark	pass	paws
sail	zebra	asleep	ozone	miss	bees
seāl	zoo	deceive	protozoa	loss	buzz
sole	zephyr	listen	busy	peace	flies
soon	zounds	clasped	business	puss	muse

This is the forest primeval, where the pines ever softly resound.
He mused upon the mystery of the sea, with its restless waves.
Ship ahoy! I see a sail upon the sunlit summer sea.
Sparrows are building their nests under the eaves of this hut.

> A ship comes sailing over the sea,
>   Sailing over the sea.
> From lands far, far away maybe,
>   With ornamets for me.

> The captain stands upon the bridge,
> As the ship sails over the sea.
> He issues orders to his men,
>   Speaks to the mate or to Pilot Ben,
> As the ship sails over the sea.

> A jolly cargo has our ship,
>   Sailing over the sea:
> Sweet spices from far Araby,
>   Bright shawls from sunny Spain, maybe,
> Sailing over the sea.

> The cargo comes from many lands,
>   Journeying over the sea.
> From Italy and southern France;
>   The Orient, too, doth perchance
> Send riches rare to me.

> I see soft leather jerkins, there,
>   Venturing o'er the sea:
> Some from London shops renowned,
>   Jade ornaments in India found.
> And sent far over the sea.

The ship soon comes to anchor,
From its travels over the sea.
The supercargo calls his men,
Ventures on board, unloads, and then!
What treasures gleam for me!

V. *Exercises for s and z sounds.*

A. -S-S-S-S   -Z-Z-Z-Z
    Ss-Ss-Ss-S   -Zz-Zz-Zz-Z
    Sss·-Sss-Sss-S   Zzz-Zzz-Zzz-Z
    Ssss-Ssss-Ssss-S   Zzzz-Zzzz-Zzzz-Z

B. -Säh-sāy-see-saw-sōh-sōō

C. -Zäh-zāy-see-saw-zōh-zōō

D. -sĭ, sĕh, să, sŭh

E. -Zĭe, zĕh, ză, zŭh.

Exercise VI. Word Drill.

S

seem	loss	niece	grass	fierce	buss
sister	miss	cost	bless	purse	lass
said	sole	ice	last	horse	house
speed	this	glass	passes	slice	
sense	spend	release	sentences	boss	

Z

zero	because	busy	dozen	zither
zounds	praise	misery	buzz	business
zephyr	easy	lose	does	honors
Zeus	gaze	graze	leaves	clothes

Exercise VII. (Problem.)

I saw a ship a-sailing, a-sailing, a-sailing,
With rubies and diamonds and emeralds in her hold,

I saw a ship a-steering, a-steering, a-steering,
With roses in red threads worked upon her sails.

Exercise VIII.   Sentences.

Does the praise please the president?
Moses sowed the zinnia seeds yesterday.
There is a season for all things.
His friends chose crackers and raisin cookies.
The boys took pictures of their new friends.
This is the forest primeval.
Buzz, buzz, buzz this is the song of the bee.
He's such a jolly fellow, in his striped coat of yellow.
Yet a great worker is he!

Exercise IX.   Word and sentence training. Lispers.

S and Z Sounds.

sent	buse	tasty	cake	brass
master	sale	case	loosen	salve
salt	dress	listen	dresser	essay
soak	sir	grease	essence	fasten
soon	seal	hiss	casket	basket
sat	Santa	sorrel	suppose	sunlight
sigh	sound	sane	sad	suit
scrub	scrunch	scrap	squirrel	scream
assure	assume	aside	asunder	asleep

I love a gold cross. The mist is rising.
Sam saw Esau saw wood. Six slender saplings.
Sit still, sir and see the purse which Santa brought me.
Susan sat on the sea shore stringing sea weeds.
One insists that he sees the ghosts of his ancestors.
I saw the saw down in Arkansas.
Come thou expressive Silence, muse his praise.

Exercise X.   Words and sentences.

zeal	bees	drizzle	Czar	burrs
zoo	zinc	prize	busy	furs
zone	azure	daze	bruise	purrs
Zion	zounds	zephyr	his	curs
zero	zenith	lose	amuse	amaze
Zeus	tease	trees	tries	prize
cows	bibs	fuse	pulls	sings

The zeal of the Czar is used in a poor cause.
The bees buzzed noisily.
The man's zeal was amazing in spite of the cause.
A soft dazzle of azure skies greeting his view.
"Zounds", exclaimed Sir Anthony "Sirrah, are you my son or
    not? Answer, you dog!" "Sir, I hope I know my duty,"
    answered Jack.
Thus I thought until my mind was dizzy.
The shapely visions dazed my tired sight.

VI. *Exercises For Nasality.*

Exercises in NG.

sting– oh	wronging– oo	awning– oh
sing– ay	meaning– ah	worrying– i
sing– i	strengthening– ay	incurring– ay
belong– oh	stocking– oh	grazing– ay
clang– ay	roaming– ah	blossoming– oo
clangor– oo	bringing– ee	clamoring– ah
cling– ee	roaring– oo	bank– ay
singing– oh	flinging– ee	bang– oo
thinking– i	breathing– ee	ringing– oh
		singer– ay

Practise sentences.
1. The singer sang many English songs.
2. It is wrong for a strong man to shrink.
3. My fingers are longer, but the bell-ringer's are stronger.
4. The donkey was tied with a long string.
5. Cataract of Lodore.
    Rising and leaping, sinking and creeping
    Swelling and sweeping, showering and springing,
    Flying and flinging, writhing and ringing,
    Eddying and whisking, spouting and frisking,
    Turning and twisting, around and around,
    With endless rebound.
For additional exercises on letter substitutions, and for

lispers, those with nasal speech, difficulty on th, s, z, ng and other sound substitutions, Birmingham-Krapp has a small manual exclusively devoted to articulation exercises, covering the consonant and vowel sounds in the English language. (C. Scribner's, Publisher, N. Y.) In dealing with foreign accent cases, Borden-Busse's SPEECH CORRECTION is helpful, (Expression Company, publishers.) Also Miss Barrows' "English Pronunciation for Foreigners," put out by the State Department of Education, Sacramento, Calif. Robert West's book DIAGNOSIS OF SPEECH DEFECTS, also contains additional exercises.

VII. *Cleft Palate Speech.*

Exercises for Cleft-Palate Nasality.

IN Blair's book "Surgery of the Mouth and Jaws," is outlined briefly an effective method of treatment for speech reëducation following the closure of the palatal cleft and hair lip. He advises beginning with the sounds which the child can already give correctly, viz; the m, n, and ng (nasal) sounds. He found that usually the cleft palatal patient could give t fairly well, so these sounds are used as a point of departure. It was discovered that the patient did not usually distinguish nasals from mutes, so that p and b were differentiated from M, "Tar" was well pronounced by most patients wearing an obturator, "stark" and "car" came next easily. He advised practising all sounds "explosively" at first.

The patient is given sounds of the following type and then sent home to practise by himself. In such cases daily lessons are urged.

Lesson I. (the mark – means breath preparation.)
```
-tar-artar-kar-arkgar-kar
-kar-arkar-arkgar-kgar-gar
```

    -kar-arkar-arkdar-kdar-dar
    -tar-artar-ardar-artar-ardar
    -tar-arsar-tar-arsar-tar-arsar-sar
    -tar-arzar-tar-arzar-tar-arzar-**tzar**
    -kar-arkar-arkpar-kpar-par
    -kar-arkar-arklar-klar-lar
    -kar-arkar-arkbar-kbar-bar
    -kar-arkar-arkmar-kmar-mar
    -kar-arkar-arkpar-kpar-par

Lesson II. (Pronounced with long *o* as in *go*.)
    -ko-okpo-kpo-po-
    -ko-okbo-kbo-bo
    -ko-okto-kto-to
    -ko-okdo-kdo-do
    -ko-okno-kno-no
    -ko-okmo-kmo-mo-
    -ko-okning, kning, ning.
    -ko-okgo-kgo-go
    -ko-okfo-kfo-fo
    -ko-okvo-kvo-vo

Lesson III.
    -kay-aktay-**ktay-tay**
    -kay-akday-kday-**day**
    -kay-akgay-kgay-**gay**
    -kay-aksay-ksay-say
    -kay-akzay-kzay-**zay**
    -kay-adklay-klay-lay
    -kay-akray-kray-ray
    -kay-akshay-kshay-**shay**
    -kay-akzhay-kzay-zay

Lesson IV. (Pronouned with long *i* as in h*i*de.)
    -ki-ikti-kti-ti
    -ki-ikdi-kdi-di
    -ki-ikli-kli-li
    -ki-ikri-**kri-ri**

–ki–ikpi–kpi–pi
–ki–ikbi–kbi–bi
–ki–ikfi–kfi–fi
–ki–ikvi–kvi–vi

Sometimes a gentle pressure exerted upon both nostrils, to show the patient how a pure oral-resonant vowel should sound, will give a certain tone standard which he may apply in seeking to give the tone free from excessive nasal resonance. Even with an opening into the posterior nares at the back part of the hard palate, when the tissue cannot be completely fused, many patients are able to compensate by training the constrictor muscles of the pharynx, and by activity of the muscles controlling the soft palate, so that a constriction or closure may be secured similar to that obtained when the soft palate closes off the posterior nares. This calls for a great deal of practise and patience.*

VIII. *Speech Training for the Deaf Child.*

(1) Formation and Development of Elementary English Sounds. Carolina Yale, Clark School for the Deaf, Northampton, Mass.

(2) Goldstein Exercises. Max Goldstein Central School for the Deaf, St. Louis, Missouri.

(3) Lip Reading. Nitchie. N. Y. School for Hard of Hearing.

(4) Muller-Walle Method of Lip Reading. Martha Bruhn. 1920. Thomas Nichols and Son.

The above texts furnish a large variety of exercises for the treatment of the deaf child in the special school or at home. We have attempted only to sum-

*For a complete description of cleft palate surgery the reader is referred to Blair's "Surgery of the Mouth and Jaws," 1917.

marize the methods employed to familiarize the speech teacher with the same, as many good books which are easy of access have been written on the subject.

The schools for the deaf in this country first taught the Sign language borrowed from the French Schools for the Deaf. Later the Lip Reading method was introduced. Miss Martha Bruhn translated into English an important work outlining the German system (Muller-Walle) and this is the text most generally used today with the adult deaf in this country. With children simpler exercises are necessary, and at most schools the Bell Visible Speech Symbols are used to illustrate the letter position and to aid the child in gaining precision in use of the tongue muscles. Because of the anatomic basis for the Bell Symbols, they will probably continue to be used by the deaf rather than the Phonetic Symbols of the International Phonetic Association, although the latter are used successfully with adults who have a remnant of hearing.

I. The child is told first to place his hand flat upon the top of his head, and to feel the vibration as he says "Z-z-z", or M-M-M. He then places the fingers lightly on the larynx opposite the place of attachment of the vocal cords, and is told to note the vibration there; also he gives the voiceless consonants s, and p, noting the difference between voiced and unvoiced consonants.

Exercise I.   The child is told to say m– m– m–.
                 Then (2) mum– mum– mum; may– may–
                 may; maw– maw– maw.

Exercise II.   The child is taught the various vowel sounds,
                 and told that the mouth must be active. The
                 kinaesthetic sensations are important at each

step. Oh– ee; oh–; ee; oh– ee, etc.

EE– oh; ee –oh, ee– oh.

Exercise III.   With nostrils closed child is taught to give the short *u* vowel like this: "up, up, up; ud– ud– ud."

He then combines first the *Oh,* then the *ee* and lastly the *u* vowel with the nasal m, n, and ng in order.

Exercise IV.   He next takes the consonants, in their phonetic grouping rather than in alphabetic arrangement.

1. p, b, m.
2. t, d, n.
3. k, g, ng.
4. l, r.
5. sh, zh.
6. ch, j.
7. f, v.
8. th (voiced) th (voiceless) as in *th*is and *th*in.
9. s, z.
10. w, wh, y.
11. H, wh, and hu (as in hue).
12. X (equals ks sound).
13. squ (equals skw sound).

Exercise V.   Practise blowing out a candle and try to develop voiced w and then the voiceless wh sound. Observe the escape of breath on the *wh* sound.

Exercise VI.   Blow: pant and try to say hoo, hoo, hoo.

Exercise VII.   Use piano to develop exercises in pitch, singing the different vowels, such as ay, ah, ee, oh, aw, oo. Piano should be used constantly in working with the deaf.

Exercise VIII.   Practise the following vowels, (1) front,
(2) mixed, (3) back vowels as shown on the
accompanying vowel diagram, illustrating
location of the tongue.

	Front		*Middle*		*Back Vowels*	
(1) We	ee (i:)	(2) burrs	er–a, (a:)	oo (u:)	(3) you
will	i (i)	about	ir–ur (e:)	oo (u)	could
get	e (e)	us	ŭ ( )	o (ou)	show
Clare's	air (ea)			aw (ɔ)	Walter
cat	a (æ)			o (ɔ)	Dot's
Friday	i (ai)			ah (a)	car
Afternoon	ah (a:)				

Chapter VII

MISCELLANEOUS METHODS IN CORRECTION

(For High School or College Use)

Selections for Voice Training, Enunciation, Interpretation, and Clear Thinking.

Near the city of Sevilla, years and years ago,
Dwelt a lady in a villa, years and years ago;
And her hair was black as night,
And her eyes were starry bright.
Olives on her brow were blooming,
Roses red her lips perfuming;
And her step was light and airy
As the tripping of a fairy.
Ah! that lady of the villa—and I loved her so,
Near the city of Sevilla, years and years ago.

A song, Oh! a song for the merry May!
The cows in the meadow, the lambs at play,
A chorus of birds in the maple tree
And a world in blossom for you and me.

Nobody looks at the clouds with a love that equals mine.
I know them in their beauty, in the morn or the even shine.
I know them, and possess them, my castles in the air.
My palaces, cathedrals, and hanging gardens fair.

Up from the meadows, rich with corn,
Clear in the cool September morn,
The clustered spires of Frederick stand,
Green-walled, by the hills of Maryland.

Chant and say: "Old King Cole was a merry old soul,
    And a merry old soul was he!
    He called for his pipe, and he called for his
      bowl
    And he called for his fiddlers, three!"

Remember March! The Ides of March remember!
Did not great Julius bleed for justice's sake?
What villain touched his body that did stab,
And not for justice?
What, shall one of us that struck
And foremost man of all this world, but
For supporting robbers, shall we now
Contaminate our fingers with base bribes,
And sell the mighty space of our large honors
For so much trash as may be graspéd thus?
I'd rather be a dog, and bay the moon,
Than such a Roman!

What, ho! my jovial mates, come on! We'll frolic it
Like fairies, frisking in the merry moonshine.

P's and Q's.
It takes a lot of letters to make up the Alphabet
And two or three of them are very easy to forget.
There's K—a funny letter—and X and Y and Z—
There's hardly any use at all for any of those three!
The vowels are the busy ones, A, E, I, O, U—
They've twice the work that all the other letters have to do!
I don't know why it is that grown-up people always choose
To tell us children to be sure and mind our P's and Q's.

A Madrigal.
    It was a lover and his lass
      With a hey and a ho, and a hey-nonino!
    That o'er the green cornfield did pass

In the springtime, the only pretty ring time,
When birds do sing hey ding a ding;
Sweet lovers love the spring.

The Life Without Passion.

They that have power to hurt, and will do none,
That do not do the thing they most do show,
Who moving others, are themselves as stone,
Unmovéd, cold, and to temptation slow,—

They rightly do inherit heaven's graces,
And husband nature's riches from expense;
They are the lords and owners of their faces,
Others, but stewards of their excellence.

Mariners of England.

O for a soft and gentle wind
I heard a fair one cry;
But give to me the snoring breeze
And white waves heaving high;
And white waves heaving high, my lads,
The good ship tight and free—
The world of waters is our home,
And merry men are we.

By the Seas.

It is a beauteous evening, calm and free;
The holy time is quiet as a nun
Breathless with adoration; the broad sun
Is sinking down in its tranquility.

L'Allegro.

Haste, thee, Nymph, and bring with thee
Jest, and youthful jollity,
Quips and cranks, and wanton wiles,
Nods, and becks, and wreathéd smiles

Such as hang on Hebe's cheek,
And love to live in dimple sleek;
Sport that wrinkled care derides,
And laughter, holding both his sides;
Come, and trip it as you go
On the light fantastic toe;
And in thy right hand lead with thee
The mountain-nymph, sweet Liberty.

Lochinvar.

Oh! young Lochinvar is come out of the West;
Through all the wide border his steed was the best;
And save his good broadsword he weapons had none,
He rode all unarmed, and he rode all alone.
So faithful in love, and so dauntless in war,
There never was knight like the young Lochinvar.

He staid not for brake and he stopped not for stone,
He swam the Eske River, where ford there was none;
But ere he alighted at Netherby Gate,
The bride had consented, the gallant came late;
For a laggard in love and a dastard in war,
Was to wed the fair Ellen of brave Lochinvar.

The Three Kings.

And so the Three Kings rode into the West,
  Through the dusk of the night, over hill and dell.
'And sometimes they nodded with beard on breast,
And sometimes talked, as they paused to rest,
  With the people they met at some wayside well.

Three caskets they bore on their saddle bows,
  Three caskets of gold with golden keys;
Their robes were of crimson silk with rows
Of bells and pomegranates and furbelows;
  Their turbans like blossoming almond-trees.

Robin Hood and Clorinda.

 As that word was spoke, Clorinda came by,
  The queen of the shepherds was she;
 And her gown was of velvet as green as the grass,
  And her buskin did reach to her knee.

 Her gait it was graceful, her body was straight,
  And her countenance free from pride;
 A bow in her hand, and quiver and arrows
  Hung dangling by her sweet side.

The Beggar Maid.

  In robe and crown the King stept down,
   To meet and greet her on her way;
  "It is no wonder," said the Lords,
   "She is more beautiful than day."

  So sweet a face, such angel grace,
   In all that land had never been,
  Cophetua sware a royal oath;
   "This beggar-maid shall be my Queen!"

My Kerry Cow.

There are red cows that's contrary, and there's white cows
 quare and wild,
But my Kerry cow is biddable, and gentle as a child.
You may rare up kings and heroes on the lovely milk she yields,
For she's fit to foster generals to fight our battlefields.
In the histories they'll be making they've a right to put her
 name,
With the horse of Troy and Oisin's hounds and other beasts of
 fame,
And the painters will be painting her beneath the hawthorn
 bough,
Where she's grazing on the good green grass,—my little Kerry
 cow.

March of the Men of Harlech.

> Hark! I hear the foe advancing,
> Barbed steeds are proudly prancing,
> Helmets in the sunbeams glancing,
> Glitter through the trees,
> Men of Harlech, lie ye dreaming?
> See you not their falchions gleaming,
> While their pennons, gaily streaming,
> Flutter to the breeze?
> From the rocks rebounding
> Let the war-cry sounding,
> Summon all to Cambria's call.
> Men of Harlech! On to glory,
> See, your banner, famed in story,
> Waves these burning words before ye,
> "Britain scorns to yield!"

An Old Castle.

> The gray arch crumbles and totters and tumbles;
> The bat has built in the banquet hall;
> In the donjon keep sly mosses creep;
> The ivy has scaled the wall,
> 'Tis the end of all—
> The gray arch crumbles and totters, and tumbles,
> And silence sits in the banquet hall.

Over the Dunes.

> Over the dunes the ducks are flying,
> And the sea breeze brings their gentle crying
> Over the dunes.
>
> Out where the sea's white hair is blowing,
> The long dark line of ducks is going
> Over the dunes.
>
> The marsh lies lone and dun and still;
> The fine sand follows the wind's will
> Over the dunes.

A gang of geese comes from the south
And heads the marsh at Mill Creek mouth,
    Over the dunes.

My heart is glad for the things that are;
And yet I long for a land afar,
    Over the dunes.

The sight of all in the word most fair,
Is the Irish land in the evening air,
    Over the dunes.

In the garden walk, by the patch of fern,
A fair haired girl waits my return
    Over the dunes.

Over the dunes the ducks are flying,
And the sea breeze brings their gentle crying,
    Over the dunes.

Little Miss Hilly.

    Oh, Little Miss Hilly of Northampton-town
    Goes walking the valleys and meadows adown;
    She looks in the brooks for the stars and the moon
    And she sings an old chanty a bit out of tune,
    Oh, Little Miss Hilly is dear unto me,—
    Is dear unto me!

    Her arms are so eager but tiny are they,
    And her fingers are agile as waters at play.
    Yet little Miss Hilly must climb a steep slope,
    Must go without laughter and live without hope;
    Must chatter and patter like leaves and like rain,
    Must shiver and quiver and ache with the pain
    Of climbing for stars and wanting the moon
    As she puts an old chanty once more into tune,

'Ere the stars will come down or the moon will reply
Except by a wing through a chink in the sky.
Oh, little Miss Hilly so dear unto me,
  So dear unto me!

Sh, L, ng and F Sounds.
"Cusha! Cusha! Cusha!" calling,
  Ere the early dews were falling
Farre away I heard her song,
  "Cusha! Cusha!" all along;
Where the reedy Lindis floweth,
Floweth, Floweth,
  From the meads where melick groweth
Faintly came her milking song.

Quit your cowslips, cowslips yellow;
  Come uppe Whitefoot, come uppe Lightfoot;
Quit your pipes of parsley hollow,
  Hollow, hollow;
Come uppe lightfoot, rise and follow;
  Lightfoot, Whitefoot,
From your clovers lift the head;
  Come uppe Jetty, follow, follow,
Jetty, to the milking shed."

While he from forth the closet brought a heap
Of candied apple, quince, and plumb and gourd;
With jellies smoother than the creamy curd,
And lucent syrups, tinct with cinnamon;
Manna and dates, in argosy transferr'd
From Fez; and spiced dainties, every one,
From silken Samarcand to cedar'd Lebanon.

S Sounds.
Noiseless as fear in a wide wilderness.

The silver, snarling trumpets 'gan to chide.

Silver sails all out of the west.

_____

Disdain and scorn ride sparkling in her eyes.

_____

How sweet the moonlight sleeps upon this bank.

L Sound.

Alone, alone, all, all, alone
Alone on a wide, wide sea!

F, L, S Sounds.

The fair breeze blew, the white foam flew,
The furrow followed free,
We were the first that ever burst
Into that silent sea.

S and Z Sounds.

Up the still, glistening beaches,
Up the creeks we will hie
Over banks of bright seaweed
The ebb-tide leaves dry.

M and N Sounds.

O mother Ida, many fountain'd Ida
Dear Mother Ida, harken ere I die,
For now the noonday quiet holds the hill;
The grasshopper is silent in the grass;
The lizard, with his shadow on the stone,
Rests like a shadow, and the winds are dead.
The purple flower droops, the golden bee
Is lily-cradled.

The gray sea and the long black land;
And the yellow half-moon large and low;
And the startled little waves that leap
In fiery ringlets from their sleep,
As I gain the cover with pushing prow,
And quench its speed i' the slushy sand.

Then a mile of warm sea-scented beach;
Three fields to cross till a farm appears;
A tap at the pane, the quick sharp scratch
And blue spurt of a lighted match,
And a voice less loud, through its joys and fears,
Than the two hearts beating each to each!

S and Sh Sounds.

A violet by a mossy stone
    Half hidden from the eye!
Fair as a star, when only one
    Is shining in the sky.

Aghast the maiden rose
White as her veil, and stood before the Queen
As tremulously as foam upon the beach
Stands in a wind, ready to break and fly.

Th Sound.

And his own thoughts, along that rugged way,
Pursued, like raging hounds, their father and their prey.

L Sound.

Lead, kindly Light, amid, th' encircling gloom
    Lead thou me on;
The night is dark, and I am far from home,
    Lead thou me on.
Keep thou my feet; I do not ask to see
The distant scene; one step enough for me.

M, N, and W Sounds.

Ho! maidens of Vienna; ho! matrons of Lucerne;
Weep, weep and rend your hair for those who never shall return.

Ho! gallant nobles of the League, look that your arms be bright;
Ho! burghers of St. Genevieve, keep watch and ward to-night.

W Sound.

O wild West Wind, thou breath of Autumn's being
    Thou from whose unseen presence the leaves dead
Are driven like ghosts from an enchanter fleeing,
    Yellow, and black, and pale, and hectic red,
Pestilence-stricken multitudes!

Gr and Br Sounds.

Great rats, small rats, lean rats, brawny rats,
Brown rats, black rats, gray rats, tawny rats,
Grave old plodders, gay young friskers,
    Father, mothers, uncles, cousins,
Cocking tails and pricking whiskers,
Families by tens and dozens,
Brothers, sisters, husbands, wives—
Followed the Piper for their lives.

S and Z Sounds.

The desire of the moth for the star,
    Of the night for the morrow,
The devotion to something afar
    From this sphere of our sorrow.

And the night shall be filled with music,
    And the cares, that infest the day,
Shall fold up their tents, like the arabs,
    And as silently steal away.

M, N, and Ng Sounds.

A feeling of sadness and longing
    That is not akin to pain,
And resembles sorrow only
    As the mist resembles the rain.

D, T, and N Sounds.

Day after day, day after day,
We stuck, nor breath nor motion;
As idle as a painted ship
Upon a painted ocean.

Th Sound.

Oh, thou art fairer than the evening air
Clad in the beauty of a thousand stars.

All in a hot and copper sky,
The bloody sun at noon
Right up above the mast did stand,
No bigger than the moon.

Tiger, tiger, burning bright
In the forests of the night.

The hungry Judges soon the sentence sign,
And wretches hang that jurymen may dine.

S and Z Sounds.

Stars of the summer night!
Far in yon azure deeps.
Hide, hide your golden light,
She sleeps,
My lady sleeps!

Bl and Th Sounds.

Blow, blow, thou winter wind.
Thou art not so unkind
'As man's ingratitude;
Thy tooth is not so keen,
Because thou art not seen,
Although thy breath be rude.

Exercises For Practice, Grade V-VIII

I.   Breathes there a man with soul so dead,
Who never to himself hath said
This is my own, my native land;
Whose heart hath ne'er within him burned,
As home his footsteps he hath turned
From wandering on a foreign strand?

II. Lord of the Universe, shield us and guide us,
      Trusting Thee always through shadow and sun!
    Thou hast united us, who can divide us?
      Keep us, oh keep us, the many in one!

III. I steal by lanes and grassy plots,
      I slide by hazel covers,
    I move the sweet forgetmenots
      That grow for happy lovers.

IV. And, sir, where American liberty raised its first voice,
and where its youth was nurtured and sustained, there
it still lives in the strength of its manhood, and full of
its original spirit.

V. From my wings are shaken the dews that waken
      The sweet buds everyone,
    When rocked to rest on their mother's breast,
      As she dances about the sun.

VI. He who reigns within himself and rules passions, desires and fears, is more than a king.

VII. The splendor falls on castle walls
      And snowy summits old in story;
    The long light shakes across the lakes,
      And the wild cataract leaps in glory.
    Blow, bugle, blow, set the wild echoes flying!
    Blow, bugle, blow, answer echoes, dying, dying, dying!

VIII. Now fades the glimmering landscape on the sight,
      And all the air a solemn stillness holds,
    Save where the beetle wheels his droning flight,
      And drowsy tinklings lull the distant folds.

Songs of Boredom.

        I wish I were a Hindoo priest,
        Existing but to pray,
        Or a jinriksha coolie—
        At least for half a day.
        I wish I were in Araby,
        With strange perfumes to smell—
        I wish I were a murderer

Whom peril sharp befell—
Or lived within a jungle
Under a blazing sky—
I make so sad a bungle
Of being always I!

Adolescence

I am so much a child that without end
I play at games and childishly believe
My own pretendings—ever fill my days
With changing faiths and loves and strange young griefs
That I invent—and though I quickly tire
Of each toy passion, still, with eagerness
As keen, I turn to the next game, and cry
"At length I love"! or "This time I believe"!
—And yet I know (sometimes) that I have found
No God who was not tenuous as smoke
Of fragrant, futile incense—never love
Of which I could say, certainly: "The years
Will not touch this"—nor any grief a month
Would not suffice to mend. And to my youth
The thought is terrible that age or death
May find me still absorbed in child's pretense—
Stretching vain hands to touch reality.

The Child's Quest.

My mother twines me roses wet with dew;
Oft have I sought the garden through and through;
I cannot find the tree whereon
My mother's roses grew.
　　Seek not, O child, the tree whereon
　　Thy mother's roses grew.

My mother tells me tales of noble deeds;
Oft have I sought her book when no one heeds;
I cannot find the page, alas,
From which my mother reads.

Seek not, O child, to find the page
From which thy mother reads.

Exercises for Agility of Tongue. Grades I. to IV.

(– indicates a pause.)

1. lah, lay, lee, –lah, lay, lee–, lah, lay, lee– lah.
2. Tah, tay, tee,– tah, tay, tee,– tah, tay, tee,– tah.
3. Same with dah, day, dee, etc.————————
4. Same with rah, ray, ree, etc.——————
5. Same with nah, nay, nee, etc.———————
6. kah, kay, kee, etc. ————————
7. gah, gay, gee, etc. ————————
8. chah, chay, chee, —————chah, chay, chee, –chah, chay, chee, –chah.
9. jah, jay, jee ———————
10. sar, say, see,——————
11. zar, zay, zee,——————
12. shar, shay, shee,————
13. zhah, zhay, zhee,——————
14. fah, fay, fee,———————
15. vah, vay, vee,—————
16. yah, yay, yee,——————
17. wah, way, wee,——————
18. whah, whay, whee,—————
19. pah, pay, pee, pah, pay, pee, pah, pay, pee, pah.
20. bah, bay, bee, –bah, bay, bee, bah, bay, bee, bah.
21. mah, may, mee, etc. —————

Exercise for Relaxation of Jaw

1. "Relax jaw, opening mouth as in a sleepy yawn. Open as I count one, and close on two, Ready! 1– 2, 1– 2," etc. (count ten times.)

Agility of Tongue Exercise.

2. "This time we are going to clean house. I want you to sweep the roof of your mouth with your tongue. Begin

at the front close to your teeth, and let your tongue sweep along the roof of your mouth, till it goes back as far as it can, and touches the highest point in your mouth! Already, 1- 2" (Sweep on one, relax tongue and bring it back to floor of the mouth, on two.)

3. "This time I want to dot the roof of your mouth with your tongue three times, once at the front as I say 1, farther back as I say 2, and way back as I say 3. Ready, begin. 1, 2, 3. Relax!"

4. "This time I want to see how far you can extend your tongue forward. Already, out, - in;" Try five times.

5. "This time let your tongue relax and lay in floor of the mouth and open mouth as in a yawn. Ready, open, close!" (5 times.)

Gymnastics for Speech Muscles.

I.

1. Lips and jaw.
   Oo, ah, ee, ah, oo, - oo, ee, ah;
   Ee, oo, ah, ---- ah, oo, ee.
2. Ah, ay, ee, aw, oh, oo.
3. Lah, lay, lee, law, loh, loo.
4. Pull upper lip down between lower teeth.
5. Bite lower lip lightly with upper teeth.
6. Alternate first upper and then lower lip.
7. Relax as in yawn to count; 1, (open); 2, (close).
8. Side to side, in two counts. (jaw movement).
9. Extend jaw forward and then relax (2 counts).

II.

Tongue Exercises.

1. Thin and flatten the tongue.
2. Thicken and round tongue.
3. Extend forward with pointed tip.
4. Extend downward toward jaw.
5. Extend up toward tip of nose.
6. Side to side; dot corners of mouth.

7. Sweep roof of mouth.
8. Dot roof of mouth.
9. Tongue from right side of cheek to left side.

III.

Relaxation and Invigoration of Soft Palate.

1. ah–ung–ah; ah, ong, ah; ee–ung–ee; ay, ung, ah.
2. ah–hung, ah; ay, hang, ay; ee, hung, ee.
3. oh, hung, oh; oo, ung, oo; i, hung, i.
4. ah, sah; ah, sah; ah, sah.
5. ah, gar; ah, gar; ah, gar, etc.

IV.

Breathing Exercises.

1. Stand with chest expanded, head erect, hips well back, knees with sufficient muscle tonus to give good poise. Breathe in, in 2 counts. Hold two counts, release in two counts.
2. Same in 4 counts. Same in 6 counts.
3. Slow intake of breath, rapid outgo in whispered "Yes" (prolonging the hissing sound, as long as breath is easily controlled) (whisper on outgoing breath, of course.)
4. Deep breath. Pronounce word, HOME, on 1 count, prolonging the humming sound as long as you can easily.
5. Rapid inhalation and slow outgoing breath, counting to 20 in groups of five, as 1, 2, 3, 4, 5. (breath) 6, 7, 8, 9, 10, etc.

S and Z Sounds.

Exercise 1. –S –S –S –S   –Z –Z –Z –Z
　　　　　 –Ss– Ss– Ss– S   –Zz –Zz –Zz –Z
　　　　　 –Sss– Sss– Sss– S   –Zzz– Zzz– Zzz– Z
　　　　　 –Ssss– Ssss– Ssss– S –Zzzz– Zzzz– Zzzz– Z

Exercise 2. Sah, say, see, saw, soh, soo.
　　　　　 Zah, zay, zee, zaw, zoh, zoo.

Exercise 3. Ay – say ee– see   oh–sow   oo–soo.
　　　　　 Ay– zay   ee– zee   oh–zow   oo– zoo.

Exercise 4. *Word and sentence practise.*

Sardine	Zane	aside	ozark	pass	paws
sail	zebra	asleep	ozone	miss	bees
seal	zoo	deceive	protozoa	loss	buzz
sole	zephyr	listen	busy	peace	flies
soon	zounds	clasped	business	puss	muse

1. This is the forest primeval, where the pines ever softly resound.
2. He mused upon the mystery of the sea, with its restless waves.
3. Ship ahoy! I see a sail upon the sunlit summer sea!
4. Sparrows are building their nests under the eaves of this hut.

Gems from President Coolidge.

1. It may be of little importance to determine at any time just where we are, but it is of the utmost importance to determine where we are going.
2. Reverence is the measure not of the others, but of ourselves.
3. Men do not make laws. They do but discover them. Laws must be justified by something more than the will of the majority. They must rest on the eternal foundation of righteousness.
4. We need more of the office-desk and less of the show-window, in politics. Let men in office substitute the midnight oil for the lime-light.

Voice Exercises for Upper Grades.

I. Chant on one note:

(long)	OO, OO, OO, OO, OO
	AH, AH, AH, AH, AH
	AY, AY, AY, AY, AY
(short)	EE, EE, EE, EE, EE
	OO, OO, OO, OO, OO

II. Say with rising and falling pitch:

pool, poor, loot. loon,
pull, full, book, cook.
pole, mole, loan, roan.
pet let, bet, met.
pine, line, mine, dine.
pin, fin, lit, tin.
pale, male, late, bale.
art, hard, mart, lard.
lawn, law, saw, paw.
pair, lair, mare, fare.
pan, man, pall, mall.
par, mar, lark, marl.
peel, beel, seal, meal.

Ask 1, 2, 3, 4, 5?	Ans. 1,
Ask 1, 2,	2, 3, 4, 5.
3, 4, 5?	Ans. 1, 2,
4, 5?	3, 4, 5.
Ask 1, 2, 3,	Ans. 1, 2, 3,
5?	4, 5.
Ask 1, 2, 3, 4,	Ans. 1, 2, 3, 4,
	5.

III. "Who killed Cock Robin? I," said the sparrow. "With my little arrow. I killed Cock Robin."

IV. "Who dares!" This was the patriot's cry,
As striding from his desk he came,
"Come out with me in freedom's name,
For her to live, for her to die!"
A hundred hands flung up reply.
A hundred voices shouted, "I"!

Vowel Drill For All Grades.

(Practise with rising and falling inflections.)

1. äh. parl, barl, larb, marl.
2. āy pail, bale, labe, male.
3. ēē peel, beel, leeb, meel.

4. aw   pall, bawl, lawb, mawl.
5. ōh   pole, bole, lobe, mole.
6. ōō   pool, bool, loob, mool.
7. ī   pile, bile, libe, mile.
8. ĕ   pet, bet, led, mel.
9. âir   pair, bare, lair, fair.
10. er, a   about, alike, again, ado, prayer, mother.
11. ir, ur   pearl, bird, lcurn, myrrh.
12. ĭ   pit, bit, limb, mit.
13. êar   peer, beer, leer, meer.
14. îre   pyre, byer, lyre, mire.
15. ow   pout, bout, lout, rout.
16. oi, oy   boil, foil, loin, soil.
17. u, ōŏ   pull, full, bush, foot.
18. ŭ   pun, bun, punt, lull.
19. ew   your, view, beauty, due, new, duke.
20. ă   pan, mat, lam, lap.
21. ŏ   pom, pol, lot, lom.

VOICE AND PHONETIC EXERCISES.
CONSONANT AND VOWEL CHART.

	P	B	M	T	D	N	K	G
aː	päh	bah	mah	tah	dah	nah	kah	gah
ei	pāy	bay	may	tay	day	nay	kay	gay
iː	pee	bee	mee	tee	dee	nee	kee	gee
ɔː	paw	baw	maw	taw	daw	naw	kaw	gaw
ɔ	pŏl	bol	mol	tol	dol	nol	kol	gol
uː	pōō	bōō	mōō	tōō	dōō	nōō	kōō	gōō
u	pŏŏ	bŏŏ	mŏŏ	tŏŏ	dŏŏ	nŏŏ	kŏŏ	gŏŏ
ʌ	pŭh	buh	muh	tuh	duh	nuh	kuh	guh
ou	poh	boh	moh	toh	doh	noh	koh	goh
æ	păt	bat	mat	tat	dat	nat	kat	gat
e	pĕt	bet	met	tet	det	net	ket	get
i	pit	bit	mit	tit	dit	nit	kit	git
ju	pew	bew	mew	tew	dew	new	kew	gew
hj	hue	hube	hume	hute	hued	hune	kewn	hugo
ai	pīre	bīre	mire	tire	dire	nire	kire	gire
uə	poor	boor	moor	toor	door	noor	koor	goor
ɛə	pair	bair	mair	tair	dair	nair	kair	gair
awə	power	bower	mower	tower	dower	nower	kower	gower
iə	peer	beer	meer	teer	deer	neer	keer	geer
ə	emperor	begin	murmur	enter	cinder	corner	flicker	ginger
ɜ·	purr	burr	myrrh	tir	dir	nur	cur	gir

VOICE AND PHONETIC EXERCISES.
CONSONANT AND VOWEL CHART.
(hw)

	Ng(ŋ)	f	v	s	z	w	wh	l
a:	ng-ah	fah	vah	sah	zah	wah	whah	lah
ei	ng-ay	fay	vay	say	zay	way	whay	lay
i:	ng-ee	fee	vee	see	zee	wee	whee	lee
ɔ:	ng-aw	faw	vaw	saw	zaw	waw	whaw	law
ɔ	ng-ol	fol	vol	sol	zol	wol	whol	lol
u:	ng-o͞o	fo͞o	vo͞o	so͞o	zo͞o	wo͞o	who͞o	lo͞o
u	ng-o͝o	fo͝o	vo͝o	so͝o	zo͝o	wo͝o	who͝o	lo͝o
ʌ	ng-uh	fuh	vuh	suh	zuh	wŭh	whuh	luh
ou	ng-oh	foh	voh	soh	zoh	woe	whoe	loe
æ	ng-at	fat	vat	sat	zat	wat	what	lat
e	ng-et	fet	vet	set	zet	wet	whet	let
i	ng-it	fit	vit	sit	zit	wit	whit	lit
ju	ng-ew	few	vew	sew	zew	wew	whew	lew
ai	ng-ire	fire	vire	sire	zire	wire	whire	lire
uə	ng-oor	foor	voor	soor	zoor	wooer	whooer	loor
ɛə	ng-air	fair	vair	sair	zair	wair	whair	lair
awə	ng-our	fower	vower	sower	zowr	wower	whower	lower
iə	ng-eer	feer	veer	seer	zeer	weer	wheer	leer
ə	singer	offer	quiver	purser	buzzer	sower	piller	mirror
ə·	ng-*ur*	f*ir*	v*ur*	s*ir*	z*ir*	w*ir*	wh*ir*	l*ir*

VOICE AND PHONETIC EXERCISES.
CONSONANT AND VOWEL CHART.

	r	sh(ʃ)	zh (ʒ)	y (j)	ch(tʃ)	i (dʒ)	h
a:	rah	shar	zhah	yah	char	jah	hah
ei	ray	shay	zhey	yay	chay	jay	hay
i:	ree	shee	zhee	yee	chee	jee	hee
ɔ:	raw	shaw	zhaw	yaw	chaw	jaw	haw
ɔ	rol	shot	zhot	yot	chot	jot	hot
u:	roo	shoo	zhoo	yoo	choo	joo	hoo
u	roo	shoo	zhoo	yoo	choo	joo	hoo
	ruh	shuh	zhuh	yuh	chuh	juh	huh
ou	roe	shoe	zhoe	yoe	choe	joe	hoe
æ	rat	shat	zhat	yat	chat	jat	hat
e	ret	shet	zhet	yet	chet	jet	het
i	rit	shin	zhin	yin	chin	jin	hin
ju	rew	shew	zhew	yew	chew	jew	hew
ai	rire	shire	zhire	yire	chire	jire	hire
uə	roor	shooer	zhooer	yooer	chooer	jooer	hooer
ɛə	rair	shair	zhair	yair	chair	jair	hair
awə	rower	shower	zhower	yower	chower	jower	hower
iə	reer	sheer	zheer	yeer	cheer	jeer	heer
ə.	*rir*						

Chapter VIII

METHODS IN TRAINING IN ENUN-CIATION, VOICE PRODUCTION, INTERPRETATION AND CLEAR THINKING

(For High School and College Use)

Exercises for Modulations of Tone and Pitch Variations.
Practise the following vowels first with rising and then with falling inflections, with well rounded, open tones. Note in the illustration that the tone is represented as covering an entire octave on the musical staff. Try to cover the same range with your speaking voice.

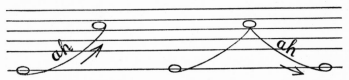

Exercise I. Practise each of the following first with rising and then with falling tone:—

ah, ah.	aw, aw.
oo, oo.	ee, ee.
ay, ay.	oo, oo.

Exercise II. Chant first on one note, and then say:—
ah, ay, ee, aw, oh, oo.
lah, lay, lee, law, loh, loo.
sah, say, see, saw, soh, soo.
mar, may, mee, maw, moh, moo.
tar, tay, tee, taw, toh, too.
dar, day, dee, daw, doh, doo.
nar, nay, nee, naw, noh, noo.

144

Exercise III. For purity of vowel quality.

Chant first, one note to each line. (as)

pool,   poor,   loon,   loot.

peel, beel, seal, meal.

pull, full, book, cook.

pole, mole, loan, roan.

pet, let, bet, met.

pine, mine, line, dine.

pin, fin, lit, tin.

pale, male, late, bale.

art, hart, mart, lard. (avoid using inverted r sound.)

lawn, law, saw, paw.

pair, mare, lair, fare.

pan, man, pallet, mallet.

par, mar, lark, marl (avoid inverted r sound).

Exercise IV. Say the above, alternating first a rising and then a falling tone, as (rising) pool; (falling) poor; (rising) loon; (falling) loot.

Exercise V. Say the following, with accent first on one numeral and then on other, (stress the underlined syllable.)

2, 3, 4, 5 ?	(Answer, falling)	
(rising) 1	1,	
3, 4, 5 ?		2, 3, 4, 5.
1-2	" 1, 2,	
4, 5 ?		3, 4, 5.
1, 2, 3,	" 1, 2, 3,	
5?		4, 5.
1, 2, 3, 4,	" 1, 2, 3, 4,	
1, 2, 3, 4, 5 ?		5.
	" 1, 2, 3, 4, 5.	

Exercise VI. Try the following for range of pitch and inflection.

Who killed Cock Robin? I said the sparrow,
With my little arrow, I killed Cock Robin.

Who saw him die? I said the fly,
With my little eye, I saw him die.

Exercise VII.

> "Who dares!" This was the patriot's cry,
> As striding from his desk he came.
> "Come out with me in freedom's name,
> For her to live, for her to die."
> A hundred hands flung up reply.
> A hundred voices shouted, "I!"

Exercise IX.

> Will they do it? Dare they do it?
> Who is speaking? What the news?
> What of Adams, What of Sherman?
> Oh, God grant they won't refuse!

Voice Exercise: Chant, prolonging the vowel tones.
"Gay go Up and Gay go Down."

> Gay go up, and gay go down,
> To ring the bells of London town.

> Bull's eyes and targets,
> Say the bells of Saint Marg'rets.

> Brickbats and tiles,
> Say the bells of St. Giles.

> Half-pence and farthings,
> Say the bells of Saint Martin's.

> Oranges and lemons,
> Say the bells of Saint Clement's.

> Pancakes and fritters,
> Say the bells of Saint Peter's.

> Two sticks and an apple,
> Say the bells of Whitechapel.

Old Father Baldpate
Say the slow bells at Aldgate.

Pokers and tongs,
Say the bells at Saint John's.

Kettles and pans,
Say the bells of Saint Ann's.

You owe men ten shillings,
Say the bells at Saint Helen's.

When will you pay me?
Say the bells at Old Bailey.

When I grow rich,
Say the bells at Shoreditch.

Pray, when will that be?
Say the bells of Stepney.

I am sure I don't know,
Says the great bell at Bow.

Selections.

East Wind   —*Brown*

I dream of a langorous, tideless shore,
  Of azure light in magic caves,
Of heathery hills with summits hoar,
  That wade knee-deep in northern waves,
Of rainbow sails like butterflies,
  That flutter to an Old World quay;
Of where a buried city lies
  Beneath the sands of Brittany.

Nay! But my own New England coast
  Pungent with wild rose, pine, and bay;
Brown marsh, white sand, gray rocks that boast
  The fiercest surf, the wildest spray!

Ho! For me,
Where the white, white sails go flashing to the sea;
And the sea wind is the east wind, as the sea wind ought
to be!

Castles in Spain   —*Longfellow*

How much of my young heart, O Spain,
    Went out to thee, in days of yore!
What dreams romantic filled my brain,
    And summoned back to life again
The Paladins of Charlemagne,
    And Cid Campeador!
The softer Andalusian skies
    Dispel the sadness and the gloom;
There Cadiz by the seaside lies,
    And Seville's orange-orchards rise,
Making the land a paradise
    Of beauty and of bloom.

Aladdin   —*Lowell*

When I was a beggarly boy,
    And lived in a cellar damp,
I had not a friend nor a toy,
    But I had Aladdin's lamp;
When I could not sleep for the cold,
    I had fire enough in my brain,
And builded, with roofs of gold,
    My beautiful castles in Spain.

Since then I have toiled day and night,
    I have money and power good store,
But I'd give all my lamps of silver bright,
    For the one that is mine no more;
Take, Fortune, whatever you choose,
    You gave, and may snatch again;
I have nothing 'twould pain me to lose,
    For I own no more castles in Spain!

Songs for My Mother   *—Branch*

    My mother's hands are cool and fair,
      They can do anything.
    Delicate mercies hide them there
      Like flowers in the spring.

    When I was small and could not sleep,
      She used to come to me,
    And with my cheek upon her hand
      How sure my nest would be.

    My mother has the prettiest tricks
      Of words and words and words.
    Her talk comes out as smooth and sleek
      As breasts of singing birds.

    She shapes her speech all silver fine
      Because she loves it so.
    And her own eyes begin to shine
      To hear her stories grow.

    And if she goes to make a call
      Or out to take a walk,
    We leave our work when she returns
      To run and hear her talk.

Across the Fields to Anne   *—Burton*

    How often in the summer-tide,
    His graver business set aside,
    Has stripling Will, the thoughtful-eyed,
    As to the pipe of Pan,
    Stepped blithesomely with lover's pride
    Across the fields to Anne.

    The silly sheep that graze today,
    I wot, they let him go his way,
    Nor once looked up, as who should say;

"It is a seemly man".
For many lads went wooing aye
Across the fields to Anne.

The House and the Road   —*Peabody*
        The little Road says Go,
        The little House says, Stay:
        And O, it's bonny here at home,
        But I must go away.

        The little Road, like me,
        Would seek and turn and know:
        And forth I must, to learn the things
        The little Road would show!

        Maybe no other way
        Your child could ever know
        Why a little House would have you stay,
        When a little Road says Go.

Scum o' the Earth   —*Schauffler*
    At the gate of the West I stand,
    On the isle where the nations throng.
    We call them "scum o' the earth".

    Stay, are we doing you wrong,
    Young fellow from Socrates land?
    You, like a Hermes so lissome and strong,
    Fresh from the Master Praxiteles' hand?
    So you're of Spartan birth?
    Descended, perhaps, from one of the band—
    Deathless in story and song—
    Who combed their long hair at Thermopylae's pass?
    Ah, I forget the straits, alas!
    More tragic than theirs, more compassion-worth,
    That have doomed you to march in our "immigrant class",
    Where you're nothing but "scum o' the earth".

Grandmither, Think Not I Forget   *—Willa Cather*
Grandmither, think not I forget, when I come back to the town,
An' wander the old ways, again, an' tread them up and down.
I never smell the clover bloom, nor see the swallows pass,
Wi'out I mind how good ye were unto a little lass;
I never hear the winter rain a-pelting all night through
Wi'out I think and mind me of how cold it falls on you.
An' if I come not often to your bed beneath the thyme,
Mayhap 'tis that I'd change wi' ye, and gie my bed for thine.
    Would like to sleep in thine.
I never hear the summer winds among the roses blow,
Wi'out I wonder why it was ye loved the lassie so.

A Vagabond Song   *—Carman*
There is something in the autumn that is native to my blood—
Touch of manner, hint of mood:
And my heart is like a rhyme,
With the yellow and the purple and the crimson keeping time.

The scarlet of the maples can shake me like a cry
Of bugles going by,
And my lonely spirit thrills
To see the frosty asters like a smoke upon the hills.

There is something in October sets the gypsy blood astir;
We must rise and follow her,
When from every hill of flame
She calls and calls each vagabond by name.

May is Building Her House   *—Gallienne*
   May is building her house. With apple blooms
     She is roofing over the glimmering rooms;
   Of the oak and the beech hath she builded its beams,
     And, spinning all day at her secret looms,
   With arras of leaves each wind-swayed **wall**
   She pictureth over, and peopleth **it all**
     With echoes and dreams,

And singing of streams.
May is building her house. Of petal and blade
Of the roots of the oak, is the flooring made,
With a carpet of lichens and mosses and clover,
Each small miracle over and over,
And tender, traveling green things strayed.

Exercises for Voice Training.

Pitch and Time.

1. And the raven never flitting,
   Still is sitting, still is sitting—
   On that pallid bust of Pallas,
   Just above my chamber door.

   —Poe

2. Once more into the breach, dear friends, once more!
   Or close the wall up with our English dead.
   In peace, there's nothing so becomes a man,
   As modest stillness and humility.
   But when the blast of war blows on our ears,
   Then imitate the action of the tiger.

   —Henry V.

3. The splendor falls on castle walls,
   And snowy summits, old in story.
   The long light shakes across the lake,
   And the wild cataract leaps in glory.

   —Tennyson

4. I remember, I remember the house where I was born,
   The little windows where the sun came creeping in at morn.
   He never came a bit too soon, nor spent too long a day,
   But now I often wish the night had ta'en my breath away.

Selected Poems.

The Elfin Artist.*   —*Noyes*

> In a glade of an elfin forest
>> When Sussex was Eden-new
> I came on an elfish painter
>> And watched as his picture grew.
> A harebell nodded beside him.
>> He dip't his brush in the dew.

A Sprig of Rosemary.   —*Lowell*

> I cannot see your face.
> When I think of you,
> It is your hands which I see.
> Your hands,
> Sewing,
> Holding a book,
> Resting for a moment on the sill of a window,
> My eyes keep always the sight of your hands,
> But my heart holds the sound of your voice,
> And the soft brightness which is your soul.

Friends   —*Johnson*

> I have a friend whose stillness rests me so
>> His heart must know
> How closely we together, silent, grow.

> I have a friend whose brilliancy inspires
>> And rarely tires
> When we two warm our spirits at his fires.

> I have a friend whose charity delights
>> In others' rights,
> We two sit talking often late at night.

> I have a friend whose discipline I need;
>> We have agreed
> That neither from this schooling shall be freed.

*Reprinted by permission from Collected Poems Vol. 3, by Alfred Noyes. Copyrt. 1920—Fred'k A. Stokes Co.

And so twice fortunate am I to find
  Friends great and kind—
Each one himself, yet part of God's own mind.

Queenstown Harbor   —*O'Connor*
  It is a lovely summer night, and I
  Stand looking from the carriage window; the train
  Starts slowly; lights twinkle through the air which rain
  Has made the softer, and the hills are changed
  To purple, then to black; they seem arranged
  By some great child who moulds a map in play.
  Darkly the waters glisten; we glide away;
  The picture passes and I settle down.
  Two hours more,—and then loved Mallow town!

Wanderlust.

Practice for the *s* and *z* sounds.

I muse oft on the eastlands,
  Its cities by the sea,
Sevilla, the cathedral town,
  Its spires high that be.

Of Florence hills, so stately,
  Its squares, and bells that chime,
The Arno, slow, meandering,
  In mellow, rhythmic rhyme.

I see the home of Dante,
  Of the Brownings, by the river,
The life-like work of Angelo,
  Of Lorenzo, the great giver.

Tangiers; narrow street ways,
  Its mosques against the blue,
I seem to traverse with my guide
  And hear his tales, with you.

I see Algeria's gardens fair,
Her motley garbed throng,
Though saddened are its women, bound
By customs ancient wrong.

Gibraltar, lofty, threatening,
And sea gulls clamoring loud,—
Again we clatter through your streets,
Traverse your tunnels proud.

My heart dreams of fair Naples,
Of Genoa by the sea,
Of Monte Carlo's lavish pride,
Her sea-air, bracing, free.

Then to the northern cities
Of Sweden and Norway,
Which speak of pride and freedom,
Of truth that lasts for aye.

But best of all are Scotland
And England of far renown,
Though we haste away to Paris gay,
'Tis to these we are most bound.

Lochinvar   —*Scott*

Oh! young Lochinvar is come out of the West;
Through all the wide border his steed was the best;
And save his good broadsword he weapons had none,
He rode all unarmed, and he rode all alone.
So faithful in love, and so dauntless in war,
There never was knight like the young Lochinvar.

He staid not for brake and he stopped not for stone,
He swam the Eske River, where ford there was none;
But ere he alighted at Netherby Gate,
The bride had consented, the gallant came late;

Robin Hood and Clorinda.

> As that word was spoke, Clorinda came by,
>   The queen of the shepards was she;
> And her gown was of velvet as green as the grass,
>   And her buskin did reach to her knee.
> For a laggard in love and a dastard in war,
> Was to wed the fair Ellen of brave Lochinvar.

The Three Kings　　　　　　　　　　　　　　*—Longfellow*

> And so the Three Kings rode into the West,
>   Through the dusk of the night, over hill and dell.
> And sometimes they nodded with beard on breast,
> And sometimes talked, as they paused to rest,
>   With the people they met at some wayside well.

> Three caskets they bore on their saddle bows,
>   Three caskets of gold with golden keys;
> Their robes were of crimson sick with rows
> Of bells and pomegranates and furbelows,
>   Their turbans like blossoming almond-trees.

> Her gait it was graceful, her body was straight,
>   And her countenance free from pride;
> A bow in her hand, and quiver and arrows
>   Hung dangling by her sweet side.

The Beggar Maid　　　　　　　　　　　　　　*—Tennyson*

> In robe and crown the King stept down,
>   To meet and greet her on her way;
> "It is no wonder," said the Lords,
>   "She is more beautiful than day".

> So sweet a face, such angel grace,
>   In all that land had never been.
> Cophetua sware a royal oath;
>   "This beggar-maid shall be my Queen!"

Beside the Blackwater   *—O'Connor*

Over the Dunes.
Over the dunes the ducks are flying,
And the sea breeze brings their gentle crying
   Over the dunes.

Out where the sea's white hair is blowing,
The long dark line of ducks is going
   Over the dunes.

The marsh lies lone and dun and still;
The fine sand follows the wind's will
   Over the dunes.

A gang of geese comes from the south
And heads the marsh at Mill Creek mouth,
   Over the dunes.

My heart is glad for the things that are;
And yet I long for a land afar,
   Over the dunes.

The sight of all in the world most fair,
Is the Irish land in the evening air,
   Over the dunes.

In the garden walk, by the patch of fern,
A fair-haired girl waits my return
   Over the dunes.

Over the dunes the ducks are flying,
And the sea breeze brings their gentle crying,
   Over the dunes.

Little Miss Hilly   *—Marks*

Oh, little Miss Hilly of Northampton-town
Goes walking the valleys and meadows adown;

She looks in the brooks for the stars and the moon
And she sings an old chanty a bit out of tune.
　Oh, little Miss Hilly is dear unto me,—
　　Is dear unto me!

Her arms are so eager but tiny are they,
And her fingers are agile as waters at play.
Yet little Miss Hilly must climb a steep slope,
Must go without laughter and live without hope;
Must chatter and patter like leaves and like rain,
Must shiver and quiver and ache with the pain
Of climbing for stars and wanting the moon
As she puts an old chanty once more into tune,
'Ere the stars will come down or the moon will reply
Except by a wink through a kink in the sky.
　Oh, little Miss Hilly so dear unto me,
　　So dear unto me!

All Round Our House   —*Holland*
I. P's and Q's.
It takes a lot of letters to make up the alphabet
And two or three of them are very easy to forget.
There's K—a funny letter—and X and Y and Z—
There's hardly any use at all for any of those three!
The vowels are the busy ones, A, E, I, O, U—
They've twice the work that all the other letters have to do;
I don't know why it is that grown-up people always choose
To tell us children to be sure and mind our P's and Q's.

A Madrigal   —*Shakespeare*
　　It was a lover and his lass
　　　With a hey and a ho, and a hey-nonino!
　　That o'er the green cornfield did pass
　　In the springtime, the only pretty ring time,
　　　When birds do sing hey ding a ding;
　　　Sweet lovers love the spring.

The Life Without Passion *—Shakespeare*

> They that have power to hurt, and will do none,
> That do not do the thing they most do show,
> Who, moving others, are themselves as stone,
> Unmoved', cold, and to temptation slow,—
>
> They rightly do inherit heaven's graces,
> And husband nature's riches from expense;
> They are the lords and owners of their faces,
> Others, but stewards of their excellence.

Mariners of England *—Cunningham*

> O for a soft and gentle wind—
> I heard a fair one cry;
> But give to me the snoring breeze
> And white waves heaving high;
> And white waves heaving high, my lads,
> The good ship tight and free—
> The world of waters is our home,
> And merry men are we.

By the Sea *—Wordsworth*

> It is a beauteous evening, calm and free;
> The holy time is quiet as a nun
> Breathless with adoration; the broad sun
> Is sinking down in its tranquility.

The Kerry Cow *—Letts*

There are red cows that's contrary, and there's white cows
  quare and wild,
But my Kerry cow is biddable, an' gentle as a child.
You may rare up kings and heroes on the lovely milk she yields,
For she's fit to foster generals to fight our battlefields.
In the histories they'll be making they've a right to put her
  name,
With the horse of Troy and Oisin's hounds and other beasts
  of fame,
And the painters will be painting her beneath the hawthorn

bough,
Where she's grazing on the good green grass,—my little Kerry
cow.

March of the Men of Harlech   *—Letts*

Hark! I hear the foe advancing,
Barbed steeds are proudly prancing,
Helmets in the sunbeams glancing,
Glitter through the trees.
Men of Harlech, lie ye dreaming?
See you not their falchions gleaming,
While their pennons, gaily streaming,
Flutter to the breeze?
From the rocks rebounding
Let the war-cry sounding.
Summon all at Cambria's call,
The haughty foe surrounding.
Men of Harlech! On to glory,
See, your banner, famed in story,
Waves these burning words before ye,
"Britain scorns to yield"!

An Old Castle   *—Aldrich*

The gray arch crumbles and totters and tumbles;
The bat has built in the banquet hall;
In the donjon keep sly mosses creep;
The ivy has scaled the wall.
'Tis the end of all—
The gray arch crumbles and totters, and tumbles,
And Silence sits in the banquet hall.

The Child's Quest   *—Shaw*

My mother twines me roses wet with dew;
Oft have I sought the garden through and through;
I cannot find the tree whereon
My mother's roses grew.
Seek not, O child, the tree whereon
Thy mother's roses grew.

My mother tells me tales of noble deeds;
Oft have I sought her book when no one heeds;
I cannot find the page, alas,
From which my mother reads.
     Seek not, O child, to find the page
     From which thy mother reads.

Songs of Boredom   —*Glascock*

          I wish I were a Hindoo priest,
          Existing but to pray,
          Or a jinriksha coolie—
          At least for half a day.

          I wish I were in Araby,
          With strange perfumes to smell—
          I wish I were a murdered
          Whom peril sharp befell—
          Or lived within a jungle
          Under a blazing sky—
          I make so sad a bungle
          Of being always I!

Adolescence.
     I am so much a child that without end
     I play at games and childishly believe
     My own pretendings—ever fill my days
     With changing faiths and loves and strange young griefs
     That I invent—and though I quickly tire
     Of each toy passion, still, with eagerness
     As keen, I turn to the next game, and cry
     "At length I love"! or "This time I believe"!
     —And yet I know (sometimes) that I have found
     No God who was not tenuous as smoke
     Of fragrant, futile incense—never love
     Of which I could say, certainly: "The years
     Will not touch this"—nor any grief a month
     Would not suffice to mend. And to my youth

The thought is terrible that age or death
May find me still absorbed in child's pretense—
Stretching vain hands to touch reality.

S and Z Sounds.

Over the roofs of white Algiers,
  Flashingly shadowing the bright bazaar,
Flitted the swallows, and not one hears
  The call of the thrushes from far, from far:
Sighed the thrushes; then, all at once,
  Broke out singing the old sweet tones,—
Singing the bridal of sap and shoot,
  The tree's slow life between root and fruit.

Now, through the copse where the fox is found,
And over the stream at a mighty bound,
And over the high lands and over the low,
O'er furrows, o'er meadows, the hunters go,
Away: as a hawk flies full at his prey,
So flieth the hunter,—away, away!
From the burst at the cover till set of sun,
When the red fox dies, and the day is done.
      And thus we sat in darkness,
        Each one busy in his prayers.
    "We are lost"! the captain shouted
        As he staggered down the stairs.
    But his little daughter whispered,
        As she took his icy hand,
    "Isn't God upon the ocean,
        Just the same as on the land?"

Ship of Sleep   —Gillespie

(s and z.)

    Silently the sea waves
    Slipped across smooth sands.
    Sadly did I wander
    In dusk-shadowed lands.

Swiftly through the darkness
Sailed a silent ship;
Looming on the sky line
Did it sway and dip.

Wings were beaten gently
By the white-winged gulls;
Porpoises like sentinels
Swam about the hulls.

Shimmering and pearl-like
Silken shadowy sails
Clung unto the high masts
Like pale bridal veils.

Sylph-like forms from other worlds,
Spirits called to me;
"We cast a charm for rest, now!
O, let thy sorrows be!"

Disappeared to westwards
That dream ship of sleep;
Wrapped in bands of silver mist,
It paled into the deep.

Silently the sea waves
Slipped across smooth sands;
Sorrow-soothed, I slept, where
Dusk hung o'er the lands.

Articulation Exercises. S and Z Sounds in Various
Combinations.

IN normal speech the sound of S is articulated by placing the
blade (or tip) of tongue against the ridge of the upper teeth,
the front of the tongue being raised in the direction of the
hard palate. The teeth may be close together or slightly separated, but the sound cannot be properly pronounced, with the

mouth wide open. Some speakers pronounce the sound with the tip of tongue lowered, but the majority of speakers use the (against upper teeth) raised position.

Exercises for Practise.

sale	seem	sign	sow	soon
sane	seed	sight	sold	soothe
saint	seal	sigh	soap	soup
same	sea	shine	sow	souvenir
Seine	seek	side	sole	superior

1. He saw the gleaming cross beside the roadside.
2. At sight of the spectacle his resentment arose.
3. I saw the picture of Saint Cecelia in this chapel.
4. Have you seen the present which Santa Claus brought my sister?
5. It is absurd to use so much ink on this paper.
6. Please place the vase on the opposite side of the shelf.
7. This is the latest atlas, I am certain.
8. The child stirred restlessly in his sleep.
9. If you insist, I shall be pleased to repeat the ghost story.
10. The ice is melting so rapidly that the skating is unsafe.
11. After a stormy session Saul listened to the songs.
12. The sounds of the zither resounded through the prison walls.
13. She saw the ship, a shining shape, upon a glimmering sea.
14. The falls of the Southland were rising and leaping as they tumbled over the sharp rocks.

Z Sounds.

Z is a voiced consonant, corresponding to the voiceless or "whispered" sound of S.

Practise words:—

zone	zeal	Zion	Zulu	zounds
Zola	Zebra	Zest	scissors	zones
observe	reserve	please	dogs	pegs
trees	gives	dozen	busy	dissolve

1. Susan was resolved to see the Zebra at the zoo.
2. I have observed the cause of his complaints against the
the laws.
3. It gives her pleasure to do kind things for others.
4. Zola was an exile from France, because of political
reasons.

S and Z Sounds.

Exercise I. –S–S–S–S   –Z–Z–Z–Z
    –Ss–Ss–Ss–S   –Zz–Zz–Zz–Z
    –Sss–Sss–Sss–S   –Zzz–Zzz–Zzz–Z
    –Ssss–Ssss–Ssss–S   –Zzzz–Zzzz–Zzzz–Z

Exercise II. –Sah, say, see, saw, soh, soo.
    –Zah, zay, zee, zaw, zoh, zoo.

Exercise III. –Ay–say. –ee–see,   oh–sow,–   oo–soo.
    –ay–zay,– –ee–zee–,   oh–zoh,–   OO–zoo.

Exercise IV. Word and sentence practise.

–sardine,	–Zane	aside	ozark	pass	paws
–sail	–zebra	asleep	ozone	miss	bees
–seal	–zoo	deceive	protozoa	loss	buzz
–sole	–zephyr	listen	busy	peace	flies
–soon	–zounds	clasped	business	puss	muse

1. This is the forest primeval, where the pines ever softly resound.
2. He mused upon the mystery of the sea, with its restless *waves.*
3. Ship ahoy! I see a sail upon the sunlit summer sea!
4. Sparrows are building their nests under the eaves of this hut.
5. The Three Fishers   —*Kingsley*

Three fishers went sailing out into the west,
    Out into the west as the sun went down;
Each thought on the woman who loved him best;
    And the children stood watching him out of the town;
For men must work and women must weep;
And there's little to earn and many to keep,
    Though the harbor bar be moaning.

Three wives sat up in the lighthouse tower,
 And they trimmed the lamps as the sun went down;
They looked at the squall, and they looked at the shower,
 And the night rack come rolling up ragged and brown!
But men must work and women must weep,
Tho storms be sudden, and waters deep.
 And the harbor bar be moaning.

Three corpses lay out on the shining sands,
 In the morning gleam as the tide went down,
And the women are weeping and wringing their hands,
 For those who will never come back to the town;
For men must work and women must weep,
And the sooner it's over the sooner to sleep—
 And goodby to the bar and its moaning.

Columbus   *—Miller*

 Behind him lay the gray Azores,
  Behind the gates of Hercules;
 Before him not the ghost of shores,
  Before him only shoreless seas.
 The good mate said: "Now must we pray,
  For lo! the very stars are gone.
 Brave Admiral, speak, what shall I say?"
  "Why, say, 'Sail on! Sail on! Sail on! and on!'"

 "My men grow mutinous day by day;
  My men grow ghastly wan and weak."
 The stout mate thought of home; a spray
  Of salt wave washed his swarthy cheek.
 "What shall I say, brave Admiral, say,
  If we sight naught but seas at dawn?"
 "Why, you shall say at break of day,
  'Sail on! sail on! sail on! and on!'"

 They sailed and sailed, as winds might blow,
  Until at last the blanched mate said,

"Why, now not even God would know
   Should I and all my men fall dead.
These very winds forget their way,
   For God from these dread seas is gone.
Now speak, brave Admiral, speak and say"—
   He said "Sail on! sail on! and on!"

They sailed. They sailed. Then spake the mate:
   "This mad sea shows his teeth tonight.
He curls his lip, he lies in wait,
   With lifted teeth, as if to bite!
Brave Admiral, say but one good word:
   What shall we do when hope is gone?"
The words leapt like a leaping sword:
   "Sail on! sail on! sail on! and on!"

Then, pale and worn, he kept the deck,
   And peered through darkness. Ah, that night
Of all dark nights! And then a speck—
   A light! A light! A light! A light!
It grew to be Time's burst of dawn.
   He gained a world; he gave that world
Its grandest lesson: "On, sail on!"

Supplement

Speech Projects for Early Grades

Chapter IX

EXERCISES AND TESTS FOR THE PRE-SCHOOL CHILD

(IN this list are included those sounds listed by the International Phonetic Association as occurring in the English Language.)

Twelve sounds are illustrated on the following page, to assist in stimulating the child to respond by giving the desired word. It is simple to grade the child's responses, with a total possible score of 108 as the standard, allowing 3 points to each of the 34 sounds. (3 × 36 = 108.) If the sound is inadequate or doubtful it may be graded 1, or if fair, it should be graded 2, or good should be graded 3 points. After the child's responses have been graded on the speech rating sheet, add the total scores (page 174). It will be easy to do this if the test sounds are underlined on a spare sheet of paper, as the child gives each response, later transferring to the classified list of sounds the responses and scores given for each sound, adding total points to secure final score.

(Several words are repeated in order to secure desired speech responses for a particular sound, in its proper phonetic grouping.)

	Consonants and Vowels	Phonetic Symbols	Object or Animal to be Imitated.	Sounds to be given by child.
1.	p	p	chick	peep–peep–peep
2.	b	b	bee	bee; buzz–buzz–buzz
3.	m	m	hum of an aeroplane	MMM! MMM! MMM!
4.	t	t	watch	tic–tic; tic–tic; tic–tic
5.	d	d	bell	ding–dong; ding–dong
6.	n	n	horse (whinny)	NNN! NNN! NNN!
7.	k	k	kitty; cat	kitty; cat–Meow!
8.	g	g	water, pouring from a bottle	gug–gug; gug–gug; gug–gug

9.	ng	ʒ	bell	ding–dong; ding–dong
10.	ch	t ʃ	watch	watch
11.	j	dʒ	rocking-horse	jig–jog; jig–jog; jig–jog
12.	f	f	fan	fan FFFFF
13.	v	v	hum of trolley-car on the wires.	VVV! VVV! VVV!
14.	s	s	a snake	SSS! (hiss) SSS! SSS!
15.	z	z	bee	buzz–buzz– buzz
16.	sh	ʃ	mother (Hush-ing sound)	Sh! Sh! Sh!
17.	zh	ʒ	humming-bird	Zh! Zh! Zh!

EASY SOUNDS.

	Consonants and Vowels	Phonetic Symbols	Object or Animal	Sounds to be given by child.
18.	y	j	wind	Yoo! Yoo! Yoo
19.	w	w	dog	Bow–wow–wow
20.	h	h	dog (after running)	H–H–H–Huh!
21.	r	r	drum	rat–a–tat; rat–a–tat
22.	l	l	bicycle bell	ling–aling; ling–aling
23.	q	kw	duck	1. quaw; quaw; quaw 2. quack–quack–quack

VOWELS.

24.	ir, ur	ə	bird	bird
25.	aw	ɔ.	watch	watch
26.	ĕ	e	bell	bell
27.	ŏ	ɔ	bell	ding–dong; ding–dong
28.	ē	i:	bird	peep–peep–peep
29.	ă	æ	sheep	ba–ba–ba
30.	ŭ		umbrella	umbrella
31.	ĭ	i	ring	ring
32.	ōō	u:	wind	Yoo! Yoo! Yoo!
33.	ä	a:	car	car
34.	ŏŏ	u	bear	woof–woof–woof
35.	ī	ai	bird	flies
36.	ō	ou	nose	blow

Score Sheet for Speech Sounds.

1. p	4. t	7. k	10. ch
2. b	5. d	8. g	11. j
3. m	6. n	9. ng	12. f

13. v	19. w	25. aw	31. ĭ
14. s	20. h	26. ĕ	32. o͞o
15. z	21. r	27. ŏ	33. ä
16. sh	22. l	28. ē	34. o͝o
17. zh	23. q (kw)	29. ă	35. ī
18. y	24. ir, ur	30. ŭ	36. ō

(Highest possible score 108). 3 points each, very good. 2 points each, fair. 1 point each, poor articulation. 36 sounds are listed. 36 × 3 equals 108, maximum score.

*Exercises to be Memorized for Enuncia-
tion, Grades I and II.*
*(Imitate the sounds made by the animals
mentioned.)*

(Say;
CAT

1. Purr, purr, purr, purr
   Jolly little bunch of fur.
   Curled up snug, like a bug in a rug,
   With a purr, purr, purr.

2. Bow, wow, wow!
   Little Dog Chow
   Funny little Chinese dog,
   Bow, wow, wow!

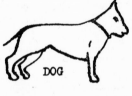

DOG

3. Hear the hen go "Cut, cut cut!"
   And the rooster crows a loud "Doo-
   dle-do."
   The Waddle-duck goes "quack, quack,
   quack"
   And the cow says, "moo, moo, moo."

Cow

4. Cut, cut, cadakut, I've laid some eggs
   for market!
   Cock-a-doodle-do! It surely isn't true!

5. The mother hen sings "cluck, cluck,
   cluck",
   And the chick replies "cheep, cheep,
   cheep."
   The mother hen steps out with a
   funny little strut,
   And the chick hops and flaps with a
   "Peep."

Hen and
chick.

6. The old horse goes at a steady jog,
   While the wheels turn round and
   round.
   Alongside trots old Rover the dog,
   With now and then a leap and a
   bound.

Horse.
Wheel.

7. The auto goes with a "honk, honk,
   honk",
   As it hurries along the drive.
   It splutters on with a "Chunk, chunk,
   chunk"
   And acts quite as if it were alive.

Auto

8. Great monster of iron, you fly o'er
   the rails
   With the bound of a lion, a-waving
   his tail.
   You puff and you rumble, you howl
   and you cry,
   Till I'm frightened and tumble, as
   you go rushing by.

Engine.

9. I like to ride in the subway trains,
   Because they make lots of noise,
   My mother takes me there, when it
   rains,
   And I think it is great fun for boys.
   Note. These words may be used for
   memory work and enunciation, but the
   words are too difficult for reading in
   Grades I and II. For words and sentences which do not involve reading
   difficulty in the first two grades, use
   words and sentences listed on pages 176-
   179.

Grade I. and II.

A. Speak the following words distinctly.

B. Put them into sentences. As, "about", "He ran about the
   house."

A (as in what)   A (as in saw)   A (as in arm)   A (as in fair)

about	all	after	air
across			
again			

B bird   book
   blue   box
   blow   boy
   black

Sentences for practise.

1. Tell me about the bird.
2. The boy ran across the road.
3. The book has black letters.

C. (The letter C has no sound of its own. It has always either the sound of K as in *c*an, or the sound of S as in *c*ircus.)

C (as in can)   C (as in circus)**

   came   company   circus
   call   Christmas   circle
   care
   carry
   clear

Ch (as in church)

   change   **child**   church
D. deep   draw   drop
   die   dress
   do   drive

Sentences for practise.

1. The company came at Christmas time.
2. Shall you carry the child to church?
3. Draw water from the deep well.
4. Do you care to go for a drive?

E. Every. I will go every day.

The words printed in this exercise are those which appear both in H. L. Thorndike's list of 2500 words in common use in early grades, (Teachers' College Record, 1921) and in the Horn-Packer list of 5000 commonest words in the spoken vocabulary of children up to and including six years of age. (Part I. Report of the Committee on Reading, pp. 161-226, Materials for Instruction, in 24th Year Book, Public School, Publishing Co., 1925.)

**C as in circus and circle does not appear in either Thorndike's or the Horn-Packer list. It is included here to explain the sounds of C.

F. face feet
   fair fire
   fall floor
   father flower
G. gold green
   good ground
   great grow
H. Had hear high hot
   hair help hill house
   hand her him how
   happy here horse hundred
I. it its is I

Sentences.

1. How fair a face is hers.
2. Help me to plant the flowers.
3. The great house is on high ground.
4. The gold made her very happy.
5. A hundred horses went to the fair.
6. My father likes to warm his feet at the fire.
7. I think it is very hot this year.

J. just* jump**

He can jump just as high as I can.

K. keep kill kind know
L. land laugh
   last learn
   late let
   letter
M. made matter milk must
   make me money my
   mark men mother

Sentences.

1. Mother let me keep the money.
2. You must learn to make a mark.
3. Keep on being kind.
4. Mother made me learn my letters.

*Thorndike list only.
**Horn-Packer list only.

N. name   no
    new*   not
    next   nothing
    night   now

O. of   on   our
    off   only   out
    old   open

P. paper   picture   play   poor
    pay   place   please   pretty
    people   plant   point   put

Sentences.

1. Please place the name on the picture.
2. The play is not a new one.
3. Did the people pay for the plant?
4. The poor child went to sleep in the open air.
5. Put the plant out on the high hill next time.
6. Take off the old paper and put on the new.

Q. quick

R. rain   ride   road   room
    reach   river   rock   run
    red   roll
    rest

S. sail   see   sing   sleep   spring   summer
    same   send   sit   small   stay   sun
    say   sister   so   stone   sweet
    saw   soft   story
                          some

Sentences.

1. My sister saw the red rocks.
2. Did you say that you would send me the paper quickly?
3. The sun is high in spring and summer.
4. I saw him sail on the river.
5. I will tell you a story before you go to sleep.
6. Sit by me and sing a song.

*The sound of —ew in the word *new* is like the sound of —ew in *few*. Do not say "noo".

T.	table	thank	till	to	train
	talk	that	time	top	try
	tell	thing		town	turn
		three			
U.	under	up	upon	us	use

V. very

Sentences.

1. He was up on the top of the train.
2. Thank you for telling us the time.
3. Wait till I come.
4. Tell us the way to town, please.
5. There are three plates upon the table.
6. Place the book upon the table.
7. Talk to me while I sit at the table.
8. The train waited a very long time.

W.	wait	we	what	who	wood
	walk	well	where	wide	work
	warm		while	will	write
	watch				
	water				

Y.	year	yet	you	your

Sentences.

1. We will wait for you a year.
2. Where did you find the wood?
3. Is your work done yet?
4. Who will work while we wait?
5. Watch the water in the well.
6. The walk is wide and well made.

Additional Sounds in our Language

Sh. shall she show
1. Shall I show you the book?
2. Did she go to the show?

ZH*   measure   treasure   pleasure

1. Give the tape-measure to mother.
2. The treasure gave him pleasure.

Ng. sing   singing   going
    spring   springing   coming
    sleeping   showing   helping

Sentences.

1. Sing a song of spring.
2. Flowers come in the spring.

Grades I. and II.

(The teacher speaks the sentences and the child gives the sound which is desired in answer to the teacher.)

Games in Phonics.

1. I growl and bark and follow my master. What am I? Answer:— (Dog).
2. I am an insect which goes "buzz, buzz, buzz". What am I? Answer:— (Bee).
3. Make a short story or sentence about the word I give you:—(vowels) *pay, pie, meat, party, road, foot, boot, saw.*
4. What word am I saying? See if you can read it from my lips. (*form* word without *sounding* it) beat, go, sew, write, pat, cry.
5. Act out each of the above if the child does not understand them.
6. Have the child tell what you are doing.
7. *(Play Xmas Tree.)* You must name the present which I

---

*Many children in the early grades do not pronounce the *zh* sound as in the above words, and it is not included in the reading vocabulary for these grades. It is probably not in the speaking vocabulary of many children in the first grades, but it is found in instances where speech is distinct at five years, and where home training favors distinctness of utterance. For this reason it is included for practice, but it is doubtful whether many children will be able to read it, and the teacher may therefore pronounce the words containing the *zh* sound, for the child to repeat after her or use in a sentence.

hand to you. (teacher has various kindergarten objects at hand, and gives one to teach child in play).

8. *Play fruit stand.* Each child buys three kinds of fruit. Name each very clearly. One child acts as fruit vendor, and the other as buyers.

9. *Play going to the bank.* Go and deposit some money in your savings account. Tell how much you wish to put in.

10. Say a word that rhymes with "make", with "cat", with "light", with "do", with "eat", (Child and teacher reverse roles.)

11. Guessing game. I am thinking of a word with "atch" in it. With –lit, in it. With –ight in it; with –ost in it. What is the word?

12. I am thinking of a word beginning with "bos". (Boston) With ma– (man).

13. Teacher: My name begins with M. What is it?
    Child: Your name must be "Marie".
    Teacher: I am a small animal whose name begins with M.
    Child: A mouse! (etc.)

14. I am something to eat. I begin with c (cake). I begin with ch. (chocolate). With l (lettuce). With s (spinach).

15. I am thinking of a boy's name. It begins with W. (William.) (Child supplies the name.)

16. I run about, pecking my food. I have feathers and cry "peep, peep." What am I? *Answer:* Chicken, bird.

17. What will you put in the collection box? It must begin with S. *Answer such as* sugar, soap, salt, spice, shoe, ship, slipper, etc.

18. Pack my trunk for China. Teacher begins game. Say "I pack my trunk for China, and I put in a ––––––––." Next takes up the game and says same, adding one article. Next continues, giving the two already named and adding a third. So on, for as long as any child in group can repeat all the names of objects. This is good memory work.

Rhymes for Speech Training. Grades I. and II.

I. *Vowel sounds, ow, aw, ă, ä.*

Bow-wow, says the dog;
  Mew-mew says the cat.
Uh, ŭh, goes the hog
  And squeak goes the rat.

Tw-whu, says the owl;
  Caw, caw, says the crow:
Quack, quack, goes the duck:
  And "Peep" the sparrows go.

These sounds we have made,
  To please you my dear:
And if they're well said,
  'Twill be charming to hear.

II. *l, r and n sounds.*

Little Robin Red Breast
  Sat upon a rail:
Niddle-noddle went his head,
  Wiggle waggle went his tail.

III. *s sounds.*

Simple Simon met a pieman
  Going to the fair:
Said Simple Simon to the pieman,
  "Please let me taste your ware."

Said the pieman to Simple Simon,
  "Show me first your penny!"
Said Simple Simon to the pieman,
  "Indeed I have not any."

IV. *h, p, gl, bl, tl sounds.*

Higglety, pigglety, my black hen,
  She lays eggs for gentlemen.
Sometimes nine and sometimes ten,
  Higglety, pigglety, my black hen.

V. T and Bl sounds

Little Boy Blue, come blow your horn,
  The sheep are in the meadow, the cows are in the corn.
Where's the little boy who tends the sheep?
  He's under the haycock, fast asleep.

VI. r, k, s sounds

Ride a cock-horse to Banbury Cross,
  To see a fine lady upon a white horse!
Rings on her fingers, and bells on her toes,
  She shall make music wherever she goes.

VII. J and B sounds

Jenny shall have a new bonnet,
  And Jenny shall go to the fair,
And Jenny shall have a blue ribbon,
  To tie up her bonny brown hair.

VIII. G, W, Ch, and Wh sounds

Goosey, goosey gander, whither shall I wander?
Upstairs, downstairs, and in my lady's chamber.

Mother Goose had a house which was built in a wood,
Where an owl at the door, for sentinel stood.

IX. P, K, ē and ĕ sounds

Peter, Peter, pumpkin eater,
  Had a wife and couldn't keep her:
Peter learned to read and spell,
  And then he kept her very well.

X. Th, Thr, S, and Sh sounds

A sunshiny shower
Won't last half an hour,
Through the rain, though,
You'll see a rainbow.

Fairy Tales for Early Grades. (Grades I and II.)

(See directions in Teacher's Key)

THE STORY OF THE SLEEPING BEAUTY.

ONCE there lived a King and Queen who wished very much for a baby princess. After a time this wish was granted and they were very happy. The King thought he ought to give a big party to celebrate the event, and so he invited all the dukes, earls and princes to attend, and also invited the fairies who lived nearby.

Now it happened that one fairy was forgotten and she became very angry at being omitted from the feast. On the day when the guests came to the party, each one brought a beautiful gift for the little princess. Each one also made a fairy wish for the baby, one wishing her happiness, another beauty, another wisdom and still another kindliness. At this moment the uninvited fairy appeared and wished that the princess, at the age of seventeen, should prick her finger and die.

Then everyone was very sad, until another fairy who had not yet made her wish, came forward. She could not undo the evil of the wicked fairy entirely, but she said "When the princess falls asleep, upon pricking her finger, it shall be granted that she shall sleep merely until a prince arrives, who shall fall in love with her great beauty and shall kiss her. Then she shall awake, and all will be well."

Then the King tried to prevent the accident which had been foretold, by banishing all the spinning wheels from the kingdom. As the little princess grew up, they gradually forgot the words of the unkind fairy.

One day, after she had passed her seventeenth birthday, the young princess was wandering about the premises, and she found an old tower in an unused part of the palace. Here she found an old woman busily spinning. So charmed was she with the whirr of the wheel that she asked to be allowed to spin. Scarcely had she started the wheel when she pricked her finger on the spindle, and fell into a deep sleep. Shortly after, every living thing in the palace also fell asleep.

Many years passed, and the palace grounds were thick with weeds, while tall branches grew up until the castle was quite hidden from view and was forgotten.

One day a brave prince came in search of adventure. As he saw the hedge, he wished to know what lay beyond, and so he hewed away the thick brambles and underbrush until he could make his way through. Then he found the deserted castle, and was surprised to find all its people sleeping. As he went from room to room, trying to find someone who was awake, he saw the sleeping princess. So charmed was he by her beautiful face and figure that he could not forbear kissing her. To his surprise she sprang up from her slumber, and at the same moment the entire household awakened.

The young prince then asked the King for his daughter's hand in marriage. The King consented and the wedding took place soon after. In a few years the Prince and Princess became the King and Queen of the land, and about this time the unkind fairy returned. So angry was she to find the Princess now a Queen indeed, that she ordered a huge barrel to be made, in which she intended to cast the Queen, and throw her into the deep sea. But the King learned of the plot, and instead of the Queen being cast into the barrel and thrown out to sea, he ordered the wicked fairy to be seized and to suffer the fate she had planned for another, and so she drifted far out into the ocean and was never seen in that land again.

Questions on the story

1. What was the chief wish of the king and queen?
2. How did the wish come true?
3. What did the king do to celebrate the happy event?
4. Whom did he invite to share the feast?
5. Who was forgotten, in sending out the invitations?
6. What gifts did the fairies make to the princess?
7. What was the gift of the evil fairy?
8. What did the last fairy do to make amends?
9. How did the king try to prevent the accident to the princess?

10. How did it happen that the evil fairy's wish seemed to come true?
11. What happened to all the people in the palace?
12. What happened to the castle after everyone fell asleep?
13. Who finally broke through the hedge which surrounded the castle?
14. How did the good fairy's wish come true, so that the princess awoke?
15. What happened to make the prince very happy?
16. Who finally became the King and Queen of the land?
17. What unexpected guest returned to the country?
18. What evil did she try to do the queen?
19. What happened when the King discovered the plot?
20. What became of the evil fairy?

CINDERELLA.

THERE was once a kind and lovely girl who lived with her stepmother and two proud step-sisters who were very ugly. The sisters were very jealous of her and made her work very hard. They named her "Cinders" or "Cinderella" because she was made to take care of the hearth,—to clean the ashes from the fireplace.

Cinderella was often made unhappy, but tried to be pleased when the sisters gave her some cast-off finery. She loved pretty gowns and was happy when she could help her sisters dress for some ball or party.

One evening the sisters came home in great joy, to tell Cinderella that they had been invited to the prince's grand ball. For days they kept "Cinders" busy waiting on them, sewing on their gowns and making ready for the great event. On the evening of the ball, after they had swept away in the great coach, Cinderella felt very lonely indeed. She sat down in front of the fire and wept because she felt so sad. Suddenly a voice close beside her said "Why do you weep"? Then in surprise Cinderella raised her head.

"I am sad," she said. "No one cares about me. I am very shabby while my sisters have beautiful clothes and go to the Prince's ball."

"You shall go to the ball, too", said the fairy. "Bring me a large yellow pumpkin from the garden. Quickly!"

Cinderella did as the fairy bade her, and lo! as the fairy waved her wand, the pumpkin changed into a gorgeous coach with yellow brocade silk lining, and bright yellow trappings.

"Bring me some rats from the cellar", said the fairy, "and a lizard or two."

Then she waved her wand, and six white horses appeared in place of the rats, while two liveried footmen, in place of lizards, sprang up behind the coach. Then she turned a large white rat into a fine fat coachman who sprang upon the front seat and cracked his whip.

"But", said Cinderella "How can I go to the ball in clothes like these?"

Then the fairy waved her wand, and a gorgeous brocaded gown took the place of her old shabby dress, and from her pocket she drew forth two glass slippers, which she placed upon her tiny feet.

"Now," said the fairy, "You are ready to go to the ball. But mind! Tell no one who you are, and be sure to leave before the last stroke of twelve, because at that moment your coach will turn to a pumpkin and your finery will all disappear."

Cinderella promised, and was off to the ball. The prince was much amazed to see the beautiful stranger, and someone told him that she was a princess in disguise. The "princess" would tell no one her story, and everybody was much pleased with her beauty and her wit, even the two proud sisters and the step-mother, who was rarely pleased with anyone except herself and her ugly daughters.

The prince danced with her many times and Cinderella had never been so happy in her life. Suddenly she heard the great clock in the hall strike slowly,—and in a panic she rushed to the stairway and fled down the steps, disappearing just before the clock struck twelve. The prince ran after her, but when he reached the gate, she had vanished, and all that he could see were some rats scampering down the street, a large yellow pumpkin by the curb, and a ragged maiden hurrying away.

Sadly he returned to the ball-room, and as he went up the stairway, he found a small crystal slipper which Cinderella had dropped in her haste. The prince made a proclamation that whoever could wear the glass slipper should become his bride, hoping in this way, to find Cinderella.

The next day a Herald went through the town, trying the slipper on the feet of many ladies in the kingdom, but always it was just a bit too large or a little too small. It never seemed to fit.

When the Herald arrived at Cinderella's home, the step-daughters and even the mother tried to squeeze their feet into the tiny slipper, but all in vain. The Herald asked if there was another person in the house, and Cinderella came forward, tried the slipper on, and then, to the amazement and envy of her sisters, drew from her pocket its mate.

Just then the fairy god-mother returned, waved her wand, and Cinderella's brocaded gown reappeared taking the place of her shabby dress. The Herald blew his horn,—led Cinderella forth from the house to where the Prince was waiting, and she went to the palace to become a real princess, and to live happily ever after.

Questions.

1. Why was Cinderella so called?
2. With whom did she live?
3. Why was she unhappy?
4. What invitation did the sisters receive?
5. How did Cinderella go to the ball?
6. What did she wear, and who made it possible for her to go?
7. How did the courtiers feel when they met Cinderella?
8. Who admired her most of all?
9. What happened when the midnight hour struck?
10. What did the prince see, when he tried to find Cinderella near the gate-way? Did he recognize her? Why not?

11. What did he find as he mounted the stairway?
12. How did he try to find Cinderella?
13. How did the Herald find Cinderella?
14. What did she draw forth from her pocket?
15. How does the story end?

Dramatization.

The above story may be acted from memory by the children, or given as a pantomime using the following characters:—Cinderella, Fairy God-Mother, Step-mother, two step-daughters, the Prince, Herald, and if the class is large enough others may act as guests at the ball.

1st scene. The Kitchen in Cinderella's home.
2nd   "   At the ball.
3rd   "   Cinderella's home again.

ROBINSON CRUSOE

ONCE there lived in England a lad whose name was Robinson Crusoe. He longed to go to sea, and all day long, he would sit gazing far over the ocean, watching the ships go in and out of the harbor. One day he hired out as one of a ship's crew and sailed away for many weeks, until one day a terrible storm arose and the ship was wrecked. Robinson Crusoe floated on a piece of wreckage until he found himself near the shore of an island, and as he was a good swimmer, he was able at last to land upon the beach. When the storm had ceased, he climbed a tall palm tree to see if there were any other boats or people nearby. But all that he saw was the disabled vessel and wreckage.

Then he decided to look about the island to see if there were other human beings there, but he found no sign of a living person. Then he made a raft and brought ashore from the wrecked vessel some food and heavy cord, some biscuits, nails and a few pieces of canvas. He also saved a gun and some gunpowder and brought ashore the only living creatures left on the boat,—a dog and a cat.

For some time, he lived in a cave, and when the food was

gone, he picked wild berries and dates from the palms, and lived upon cocoanut milk, fish and birds which he was able to catch. One day he found a baby goat which he brought home, and after that he added goat's milk and cheese to his food.

One day he was surprised to see foot-prints in the sand. He was afraid that cannibals were near, for he saw a boat in the cove. Then he saw a poor black man rushing towards him with swift-footed men with arrows following rapidly. Robinson Crusoe then fired his gun, and at the first flash, the savages turned and ran, while the escaped slave fell at Robinson Crusoe's feet, and sobbed his gratitude.

This happened on Friday and so Crusoe named the man "Friday". The black man became a good servant, and learned to cook, to sew, and to do many other useful things. Together they made a boat, which was finished after many long weeks, and then they sailed around the island. They climbed to the hilltop at the center of the island, and attached a pole to the tallest palm tree, and there they fastened a piece of a sail, which flapped in the wind like a flag. They hoped it would attract boats which might sail near the island. But it was many long days before they saw a boat. From the hilltop they saw it approaching, and with fear and joy they watched it. When the boat came near, Robinson saw that the men were intending to land upon the island, and so he and Friday hastened down to the beach to make signs of welcome.

The sailors landed, and after a feast, they took Robinson Crusoe and his man Friday on board the big boat with them and sailed away. Robinson Crusoe returned to England, where he lived for many years.

Questions.

1. What was Robinson Crusoe's native land?
2. What did he long to do?
3. How did his dream come true?
4. What happened to the ship, at sea?

5. What happened to Robinson Crusoe? To the rest of the crew?

6. How was Robinson Crusoe saved?

7. What did he find upon the island, to supply him with food?

8. How did he make use of the supplies on the wrecked ship?

9. In what kind of a habitation did he live?

10. What did he discover in the sand one day?

11. How did he find his man "Friday"?

12. What did the two build, after much hard work?

13. How did they try to attract the attention of sailing vessels, so to hope for a rescue?

14. Did a boat really come at last?

15. How do you think Robinson Crusoe felt, when he saw white men again, and knew that he could go home?

16. How do you think you would have felt?

17. Did Robinson Crusoe act as if he were glad to see them? How do you know?

18. To what country did Robinson Crusoe go to spend the rest of his life?

Poems and exercises for speech correction, arranged by grades.
Grade III.

1. Little Bo Peep has lost her sheep,
   And can't tell where to find them.
   Leave them alone and they will come home,
   And bring their tails behind them.

2. Old King Cole was a merry old soul,
   And a merry old soul was he!
   He called for his pipe and he called for his bowl,
   And he called for his fiddlers three.

3. Hickory, dickory, dock,
       The mouse ran up the clock,
   The clock struck one and down he spun,
       Hickory, dickory, dock.

4. Twinkle, twinkle, little star,
   How I wonder what you are,
   Up above the world so high,
   Like a diamond in the sky.

5. Dark brown is the river,
   Golden is the sand.
   It flows along forever, with trees on either hand.
   Green leaves afloating, castles of the foam,
   Boats of mine aboating,
   Where will all come home?

6. Goosey, goosey, gander,
   Whither shall I wander?
   Upstairs, downstairs,
   In my lady's chamber?

7. Peeping, peeping, here and there,
   In lawns and meadows everywhere
   Coming up to find the spring,
   And hear the robin red-breast sing.

8. A burdock once bewailed its fate,
   And wished it weren't so prickly.
   "I'm good for nothing, out of date,
   Just full of burrs and sticky!"
   Some ladies just now passed me by,
   For a large purple aster,
   "Look out for burrs," I heard one cry,
   "To touch one is disaster!"

9. Just then, a sunny lass came near;
   "See, Nurse, those burdock plants!
   I'll gather in my apron here,
   To see burrs makes me dance.

I'll have such chairs and tables made,
My doll's house will be filled."
The burdock bush, no more afraid,
With joy was fairly thrilled.

"I am of use! I am of use!"
He cried aloud in glee.
"No longer will I hear abuse.
They've found the place for me!"

10. In winter I get up at night,
And dress by yellow candle-light.
In summer quite the other way,
I have to go to bed by day.
I have to go to bed and see
The birds still hopping on the tree,
Or hear the grown-up people's feet
Still going past me in the street.

11. The gingham dog and the calico cat
    Side by side on the table sat.
'Twas half-past-twelve,
    And what do you think?
Not one nor t'other had slept a wink!

Now, mind I'm only telling you,
What the old Dutch clock declares is true.

12. The Owl and the Pussycat went to sea
    In a beautiful peagreen boat;
They took some honey and plenty of money
    Wrapped up in a five-pound note.
The owl looked up to the stars above
    And sang to a small guitar.
"O lovely pussy, O pussy my love,
    What a beautiful pussy you are,
        You are,
    What a beautiful pussy you are!"

Grade IV.

1. The friendly cow all red and white,
   I love with all my heart;
   She gives me cream with all her might,
   To eat with apple-tart.

2. She wanders lowing here and there,
   And yet she cannot stray,
   All in the pleasant openfair,
   The pleasant light of day.

3. "O look at the moon!
   She is shining up there;
   O mother, she looks
   Like a lamp in the air!"

4. I saw you toss the kites on high
   And blow the birds about the sky;
   And all around I heard you pass,
   Like ladies' skirts across the grass—
   O wind, a-blowing all day long,
   O wind, that sings so loud a song!

5. Buzz, buzz, buzz, this is the song of the bee.
   His legs are of yellow; a jolly good fellow,
   And yet a great worker is he.

6. Breathes there a man with soul so dead,
   Who never to himself hath said,
   This is my own, my native land.

7. There was a tree, stood in the ground,
   The prettiest tree, you ever did see,
   With the green grass growing all around.

   Now in this tree there was a branch,
   The prettiest branch you ever did see—
   The branch on the tree and the tree in the ground,
   And the green grass growing all around.

8. "Oh Mary, go and call the cattle home,
   And call the cattle home,
   And call the cattle home,
   Across the sands of Dee."
   The western wind was wild and dank with foam,
   And all alone went she.

Grade V.

1. Great, wide, wonderful, beautiful world,
   With the wonderful water around you curled,
   And the wonderful grass upon your breast,
   World, you are grandly and beautifully dressed.

2. 'Twas the night before Christmas, when all through the
       house
   Not a creature was stirring, not even a mouse.
   The stockings were hung by the chimney with care,
   In hopes that St. Nicholas soon would be there.

3. I saw a ship a-sailing, a-sailing, a-sailing, on the sea;
   Her masts were of the shining gold, her decks of ivory;
   And sails of silk, as soft as silk, and silvern shrouds had she.

   And round about her sailing, the sea was sparkling white.
   The waves all clapped their hands and sang, to see so
       fair a sight.
   They kissed her twice, they kissed her thrice,
   And murmured with delight.

4. The Man in the Moon, as he sails in the sky
   Is a very remarkable skipper.
   But he made a mistake, when he tried to take
   A drink of milk from the dipper.

   He dipped right into the Milky Way
   And slowly and carefully filled it
   The Big Bear growled, and the Little Bear howled,
   And scared him so that he spilled it.

5. "Peep," says the little bird,
"Peep," says she,
Out in her nest in the maple tree.

6. Oh! Columbia the gem of the ocean,
The home of the brave and the free,
The shrine of each patriot's devotion,
A world offers homage to thee.

7. O where and O where is your Highland laddie gone?
O where and O where is your Highland laddie gone?
He's gone to fight the foe for King George upon the
throne
And it's O in my heart that I wish him safe at home.

8. Have you ever heard the wind go, "Yo-o-o-o-o-o-?"
'Tis a pitiful sound to hear,
It seems to chill you through and through,
With its "Y-o-o-o-o-, Yo-o-o-o-o- Y-o-o-o-o-o-o!"

Grade VI

1. We are airy little creatures,
All of different voice and features;
One of us in glass is set,
One of us you'll find in jet.
'Tother you may see in tin,
And the fourth a box within,
If the fifth you should pursue,
It can never fly from you.

2. Said the Wind to the Moon, "I will blow you out;
You stare in the air
Like a ghost in the chair—
Always looking what I am about.
I hate to be watched; I will blow you out."

3. What cheer is there that's half so good,
    On a snowy winter's night,
As a dancing fire of hickory wood,
    And an easy chair in the light,
With a rosy-cheeked apple, mellow and sweet,
And pop-corn, dancing in the heat.

4. Oh such a commotion under the ground,
When March called "Ho, there, Ho!"
Such spreading of rootlets far and wide,
Such whispering to and fro.

5. By the flow of the inland river,
    Whence the fleets of the iron have fled,
Where the blades of the grave-grass quiver,
    Asleep are the ranks of the dead;
Under the sod and the dew,
    Waiting the judgment day,
Under the one, the Blue;
    Under the other, the Gray.

Grade VII.

1. Behind him lay the gray Azores,
    Behind the gates of Hercules;
Before him, not the ghost of shores,
    Before him, only shoreless seas.
The good mate said; "Now must we pray,
    For lo! the very stars are gone.
Brave Admiral, speak, what shall I say?"
    "Why, say 'Sail on, Sail on! Sail on!'"

2. Tell me not, in mournful numbers,
    Life is but an empty dream,
For the soul is dead that slumbers
    And things are not what they seem.

3. A good sword and a trusty hand, a merry heart and true.
   King James' men shall understand
   What Cornish lads can do.
   And have they fixed the where and when?
   And shall Trelawney die?
   Here's twenty thousand Cornish bold, shall know the
   reason why!

4. Come one, come all! This rock shall fly
   From its firm base, as soon as I.

5. Lord of the universe, shield us and guide us,
   Trusting Thee always, through shadow and sun.
   Thou hast united us, who shall divide us?
   Keep us, oh keep us, the many in one.

6. Aye, tear her tattered ensign down.
   Long has it waved on high,
   And many an eye has danced to see
   That banner in the sky.

Grade VIII.

1. Have you seen an apple orchard in the spring, in the
   spring?
   An English apple orchard in the spring?

2. Self-reverence, self-knowledge, self-control,
   These three alone lead life to sovereign power.

3. Stand! the ground's your own, my braves,
   Will ye give it up to slaves?
   Will ye look for greener graves?
   Hope ye mercy still?

4. I halted at a pleasant inn
   As I my way was wending—
   A golden apple was the sign,
   From knotty bough descending,

5. So the Deacon inquired of the village fold
   Where he could find the strongest oak,
   That couldn't be split nor bent nor broke,—
   That was for spokes and floor and sills;
   He sent for lancewood to make the thills.

6.   The Fox and the Grapes.

Once upon a time there were some long vines, growing
about poles, in long rows and lovely purple grapes hung from
the vines in rich clusters. One bright day, when the air was
rather dry and warm, a fox, who was very thirsty, stood looking at the vines and said,—

"What a pity the grapes grow so high! I should enjoy them
very much if only I could get at them". So he made a leap, but
fell back to the ground without reaching the luscious fruit. At
last he fell upon a sharp rock and was bruised. Then he turned
away with a sneer saying,

"Sour grapes! I don't wish for you at all. You are so sour
that even the birds won't eat you!"

Miscellaneous Exercises.
*(Grades III and IV. For Practise in Speech Composition and
Story Telling.)*

1.   The Fox and the Crow.

There was once a crow with a piece of cheese in her beak.
She was sitting high in a tree, when a fox spied her and
thought, "How I should like some of that cheese!" Then he
walked beneath the tree and said, "Good morning, Madam!
How fine your feathers look this morning. I am sure your
voice is quite as beautiful. Please sing one song for me!" The
crow was so flattered at this bit of praise that she opened her
beak to sing. The cheese dropped to the ground and the fox
picked it up, calling out "Thank you, Madam Crow! You
need not sing for me any more. I only wanted a piece of
cheese!"

2.   The Little Red Hen.

Little red hen was in a barnyard with her chicks, when she found some grains of wheat.

"Who will plant the wheat?" said she.

"Not I", said the Goose.

"Not I", said the Duck.

"I will", said little red hen, and she proceeded to plant the wheat.

When it was ripe she said, "Who will take this wheat to mill?"

"I won't," said the Goose.

"Nor I", said the Duck.

"I will, then," said the little red hen, and she took the wheat to the mill.

Then she brought home some fine white flour and she said, "Who will make the flour up into bread?"

"Not I," said the Goose.

"Nor I," said the Duck.

"Very well, then I will", said red hen.

When the bread was baked she said, "Who will eat the bread?"

"I will," said the Goose.

"I will", said the Duck.

"No, you won't!" said little red hen. "You wouldn't help me, so I intend to eat it all myself. Cluck, cluck". Then she called her chickens to help her.

3.   The Fox and His Tricks.

A cat once met a fox in the woods. "Ah", said Mr. Fox. "She is talked of in the world a great deal. I will speak to her". Then he said, "Good morning, Puss. How are you this fine day? How many tricks do you know?" "Only one", said Puss. "If the hunters are behind me, I can jump into a tree and save myself." "Is that all", cried the Fox. "Why I know a hundred tricks and have a whole sack full of cunning." At that moment a hunter with a pack of hounds approached. Puss sprang nimbly into a tree, where she quite concealed herself in the foliage. The fox ran as fast as he could, but he was soon caught. "Turn out your sack full of tricks, Mr. Fox," cried Puss. "Turn out your sack!" but the hounds had caught him and held him fast. One good trick is better than a thousand poor ones.

4. The Sun and the Wind.

Once the sun and the wind quarrelled as to which was the stronger. While they were arguing a traveller approached, wearing a cloak.

"Here is a chance to find out which is the stronger", said the Wind. "Let us see which is able to make the man remove his coat".

"Very well", said the Sun.

The wind began to blow with all his might, but the more he blew, the tighter the traveler wrapped his coat about him.

At last he gave up the effort and the sun began to shine with all his might upon the man's shoulders. As it grew hotter, the man unfastened his cloak and finally took it off. The sun had won the wager.

5. The Miser.

There was once a miser, who hid his gold at the foot of a tree. Every few days he dug it up and looked at it. One night a robber found the gold and ran away with it. Next morning the miser came to look for his treasure, but found only the empty hole. Then he raised such a cry that the neighbors came rushing to learn what was the matter. Sorrowfully he told them of his loss.

"Did you ever use any of the gold", one of them asked.

"No", answered the miser, "I only looked at it".

"Then come again and look at the empty hole. It will do you as much good as the useless gold."

Easy Sentences for Grades III. to V. With Consonant Sounds.

1. h.   Can he unharness the horse?
2. f   Fred offered me a cream puff.
3. v   That is a very good piece of velvet which you have.
4. p   Will you place the apple and the cup on the table?
5. b   The bear was rubbing against the corn crib.
6. m   My mother is combing her hair in the next room.
7. t   Tom pulled the button off his new coat.
8. d   Did you tell the riddle to Ted?
9. n   Now we will go to dinner, as it is noon.
10. k   Kitty has a basket in that nook.
11. g   A great many years ago there was a magic rug.
12. ng I heard her singing a sweet song.
13. ch The child was scratching the table with a match.
14. j   Jennie enjoys making fudge.
15. s   I saw your sister this morning.
16. z   At zero the leaves began to freeze.
17. sh She is washing the dish.
18. zh Where is the new tape-measure?
19. w-wh. I saw Will turn the wheel.
20. l   He pulled the ladder from the wall.
21. r   The rat had a merry time of it.
22. y   Bring me the yellow box.
23. x (ks) I asked for some extra help on the hard example.
24. qu (kw) The queen was not acquainted with them.
25. br-tr. The bright red bird flitted from tree to tree.
26. bl. The big black cat chased the little red squirrel.
27. spr.-pt. Little Dandelion slept until the warm spring days appeared.

Fables and Folk Tales, Grades V to VIII.

1.   The Boy and the Nuts.

One day a selfish Boy saw a jar of nuts. He put his hand into the jar and grasped as many as his hand could hold. As the mouth of the jar was small he could not pull his hand out, so he became frightened and began to cry. "I can't get my hand out!" he whined. A boy standing near said, "Take only half as many, and you can easily get your hand out!"

2.   The Selfish Dog.

Once a cow who was hungry came to a manger full of hay. But a dog was lying there, snarling and barking, and would not let the cow come near the hay. "Mr. Dog", mooed the cow, "How selfish you are; you cannot eat the hay yourself, and you will let no one else have any of it."

3.   The Crow and the Pitcher.

Once a crow who was very thirsty found a pitcher with a little water at the bottom which he was unable to reach. He tried to overturn the pitcher, but it was too heavy. "Ah, ah! I know what I'll do," he said. So he gathered up pebbles from the ground, and one after another dropped them into the pitcher until the water gradually reached the top. Then the wise crow was able to drink all the water he wanted.

4.   The Shepherd Boy and the Wolf.

Once there was a boy who took care of a flock of sheep near a town. One day, when some men were working in the town, they heard the boy call, "Wolf! Wolf! The wolves are eating my sheep!" The men dropped their work in great haste and ran up the hill, but found no wolf among the sheep. The boy laughed aloud, "Ha, ha! I only called you for a joke!" he said. Once again he called them, and again they came, but found no wolf. This time the men were very angry and said to the boy, "Do not call us again, for we will not come." One day a wolf really came and began to devour one of the lambs. The boy in terror called "Wolf, wolf! A wolf is really eating my sheep!" But the men said, "He can't fool us again", and they shook their heads and continued their work. So the foolish boy lost his sheep and then he lost his job tending sheep, because his master found out that he could not believe what the boy said. "A boy who tells lies even in fun," he said, "may not always be believed when he tells the truth."

5.   The Persian and His Sons.

Once a Persian ruler, who lived in a great palace with his three sons, had a beautiful pearl which he decided to give to the son who showed himself to be the noblest. He called the three boys to him and asked each to tell the best deed he had performed within the last month. The eldest said, "As I was travelling in a far country, a merchant entrusted me with many jewels, and he did not count them. I might easily have kept one or two and they would not have been missed. I kept the jewels safely and delivered them all as though they had been my own." "My son," said the ruler, "You were honest and did a noble deed."

"Father," said the second son, "as I was walking, the other day, I saw a child playing beside the lake, and even as I watched, the child fell into the water. I plunged in and saved the child from drowning." "You have done your duty," said the father, "and you too have done a noble deed."

"Father," said the third boy, "as I crossed over the mountain I saw a man who had done a great wrong, sleeping near the edge of a deep pit. I would have walked by without a word, but something within me called out to go back and awaken him, lest he fall, and be killed. I did this, knowing all the time that the man would probably not understand and would be angry with me, as indeed was the case." "My son," cried the father, "your deed was the noblest of them all. To do good to an enemy without hope of reward is indeed the noblest of all. The pearl belongs to you!"

6.   Why the Bear has a Stumpy Tail.

One day a Bear met a fox, who was slinking along with a string of fish he had stolen. "Where did you get those nice fish?" said the bear. "That's telling," laughed the fox, "but if you want some, just cut a hole in the ice, stick your tail down into the water, and soon you will get a nibble. The longer you hold your tail there the more fish you will catch. Then all at once you must pull your tail out sideways, with a strong jerk." The bear went down to the ice and held his tail a long long time in the hole in the ice until it was frozen fast in. Then he jerked it out with a side pull, and his tail snapped short off. And the people used to think that was the reason why the Bear's tail was short.

7. The Conceited Grasshopper.

One day a very young grasshopper and an old rooster met in a field. "I can jump higher than anybody," chirped the grasshopper. "All right, let me see you do it," said the Rooster, at the same time opening his mouth as if he meant to yawn. "Here I go, then," cried the grasshopper. He jumped so high he landed right in the mouth of the rooster, who gulped him down. That was the end of the boasting grasshopper.

8. The Lion and the Mouse.

One day a lion was lying fast asleep in the woods, when a mouse ran across his nose, and frightened him. The lion quickly caught the little mouse in his paws. "Please do not eat me, Mr. Lion," said the mouse. "I would not make even a mouthful. Let me go, and some day I will repay you." This made the lion roar with laughter, but he let the mouse go. Not long afterward the good lion was caught in a net, in the jungle. He roared aloud in deep distress. The mouse heard him and ran to his assistance. "Now, Mr. Lion," said the mouse, "I will help you to get away." "How can you?" roared the lion. "Do you not see that I am caught fast in the net?" Quickly the mouse began to gnaw with his sharp teeth, and after a time the lion was free. The mouse laughed as he scampered away, saying, "Little friends may help as much as great friends. I did help you after all, you see!"

Legends of the Days and Hours. Grades IV-VIII.
See Directions in Teacher's Key.

I. The Days.

Of course you have heard the story of how the world was created, according to the Scripture, in six great periods, called by the ancients "Days", and how rest was to take the place of work, on the seventh great day. From this, we have our seven-day-week, which the Egyptians first established. Then Greece and Rome spoke of the seven days and divided their calandar into seven-day periods about the time when Christ appeared on earth.

But did you know that it was really to the Germans, or Saxons, that we owe the names of the days of the week? Sunday for instance, means the Sun's Day. On this day Apollo, the Sun God, may be seen in his chariot as he drives his steeds across the sky from East to West. He drives in a golden car, ablaze with light and drawn by a tortoise. Before him goes Aurora, goddess of the dawn, to scatter flowers, and touch with rosy fingers the mountain peaks and clouds. This is the myth which the ancient Greeks believed and which they told to their children long years ago.

Monday means "Moon's Day". By many people it was believed, long years ago, that the Moon was the goddess Diana's car, gilded in silver light, shining far above us in the heavens, as she drives across the sky, lest mortals be deprived of light entirely, while Apollo is out of sight.

Tuesday was called in honor of the war god Mars. Mars is supposed to have been the first great warlike leader of the destinies of nations. The name is more like the Saxon god's name than like that of Mars, the god of the Greeks. The Saxons called it "Tuesco."

Wednesday, renamed from Woden's Day, was so called in honor of Woden, the Saxon god, who was much like Mercury, the messenger of the gods on Mt. Olympus, where the Greek gods were supposed to dwell. He had a reputation for being warlike and a great fighter.

Thursday, or Thor's Day, was called in honor of the Saxon god Thor, (Pronounced like "Tor") who was like the Greek called the Thunderer, and the most powerful of all the gods on Mount Olympus.

Friday was called for Freya or Friga, the goddess of love and beauty. It meant the same as Venus' Day, as Venus was the Greek name for this goddess.

Saturday sounds much like the name of the god Saturn, from which it is taken. It means Saturn's Day. One of the large stars was also named for the god Saturn.

II. Hours.

In most of the civilized world the day is divided into twenty-four hours. Before watches and clocks were invented, the time was kept by watching the shadows of the sun upon a dial. Often these were found in the garden. Always where the sun's shadow would fall aslant the surface, and at regular intervals, marks were made upon the metal surface, to show the time of day, so people read the hour, as you and I read the face of the clock.

The Chinese people have only twelve hours in their day, that is—one of their hours is like two of those we know. Ancient people divided the day and night, as we do, into twelve parts, called hours.

Aurora, the goddess of the Dawn, is supposed to be the patroness of the first hour of the day, while Minerva, the war-goddess, with the Owl or bird of night, presides over the first hour of the night.

Sometimes ancient people used an hour-glass, filled with sand, to tell the passing of an hour, as it was supposed to take an hour for the sand to run from one part of the glass, through a narrow opening into the other half of the glass. This was much the same, as the small glass, large at either end, but connected by a narrow glass tube, which your mother some-times uses in the kitchen to tell time, when she wishes to boil an egg for three minutes, as it is supposed to take exactly three minutes for the sand to run from one half of the glass through the narrow opening, into the lower half.

Oral Review.

1. Tell me the meaning of each of the days of the week.
2. Into how many hours is the day (including night also) divided?
3. Is this true in all nations?
4. What goddess is supposed to govern the first hour of the day?
5. Of the night? Why?
6. How did the ancients tell the time of day before clocks were made?
7. Do you ever see dials of this type today? Where?
8. Have you ever seen a Sun-dial? What did it look like?

Miscellaneous Exercises and Projects for Speech Training
Grades III-VIII
See Directions in Teacher's Key

1.   The Story of the Seasons.

Once upon a time Spring, Summer, Autumn and Winter had a quarrel. Each wished to be greater than any of the others. Spring said, "I am the best because I have a pretty green dress, all covered with bright colored flowers. The birds all fly back from the south when they hear that I am coming, and the Sun sends his beams down to make me grow."

Summer said, "No, I am the best; do I not bring the ripe strawberries and cherries and corn? I ripen the wheat and feed all the world. None of the rest of you can do that!"

Autumn cried, "I bring the clusters of purple grapes, the apples and peaches; I bring brilliant colors to the maples and the oak trees, and best of all I bring Thanksgiving Day." Then all three cried out "Now what can you say, old dreary Winter? What can you do?"

Then old Winter said, "It is true I cannot bring the green grass, but I have a soft dress which children love, because it is so white and fleecy. I can't make flowers grow, but I bring the diamond icicles and I freeze the ponds and rivers on which the children love to skate and slide. I bring warm fires and make happy homes. But best of all I bring Christmas and Santa Claus who brings the Christmas trees and Christmas stockings to be filled."

Then all Earth's children, who were listening said, "We love Spring and Summer and Autumn, but we love old Winter best of all"!

2.   Three Wishes!

There once lived a man and his wife, in a small cottage by the edge of a wood. They were very poor and had very little to eat. The man said "How I wish we were rich, or that some good fairy would say to me, 'What do you wish? I will give you anything you want.' Then I would wish for something that would make us happy all our lives." "So would I," said his wife.

Scarcely had they finished speaking when a fairy appeared, "I heard your wish", she said, "Wish for three things, and I will bring them to you. You may only ask for three, so wish for something good."

Then the couple tried to think very hard about what they wanted most of all in the world. The woman said, "Oh, if I only had a fine sausage!" A sausage came flying into the room and alighted on her plate, and she heard a small voice say, "Now you have one wish."

Her husband was angry and said "What a wish! I only wish that sausage was tied to your nose!" The sausage hopped off the plate and hung from his wife's nose, so the second wish was fulfilled.

This made the woman weep, until she exclaimed, "Oh, if that sausage was only a thousand miles away!" At this the sausage immediately flew out of the window and the third wish was fulfilled. The couple saw the folly of their foolish wishes and remained satisfied with what they had.

3.   Diamonds and Toads.

Once there were two sisters who were very lovely, but they were not at all alike. One was haughty and proud and said unkind things, so that people did not like her. The other was gentle and good, and always thoughtful of other people. It happened that the mother of the two girls liked the proud, unkind daughter best. She imposed upon the younger daughter and gave her many hard tasks to do. Twice each day she went to the spring to fetch water. It was a long walk and she was often very tired. One day a poor old woman came by and asked her for a drink. The girl filled the pitcher with cool, sparkling water, and held it while the woman drank.

The old woman was a fairy, who was hidden in rough garments. She said to the girl, "As you have been kind to me, I intend to make you a present, whenever you speak kind words, a rose or a diamond shall fall from your lips." Then the fairy vanished. So the girl took her pitcher and went home. Her mother was angry because she was late, but she only replied "I'm sorry to have stayed so long." As she spoke jewels fell from her lips and the mother and daughter hastened to pick them up. Then the girl told them about the woman at the fountain, and the mother sent her other daughter there to receive a gift.

When the older daughter reached the fountain she found, instead of the shabby old woman a richly dressed stranger, who asked her for a drink, but the girl said proudly, "I did not come here to pour water for you. Pour it for yourself." "You are very impolite", said the fairy, for it was really she. "Whenever you speak hereafter, toads and lizards shall fall from your mouth." Then the girl went home. But when the mother learned what had happened she was very angry at the younger sister because she thought she had caused the trouble, and she drove here away. Then the kind fairy found her crying, and comforted her and took her far away, where she became very happy.

It was a long time before the unkind sister learned to be kind even though a toad or lizard fell from her lips whenever she said an unkind word. But at last, remembering her gentle sister and her ways she learned to speak kindly and to be gentle, until she came to be loved by her neighbors almost as much as the younger sister had been.

4.   The Story of the King with the Golden Touch.

Once there lived a king who was very rich. It took him a long time to count all of his gold pieces, yet he was always seeking to become richer. One day he met a stranger who said, "Why do you look so sad"? and the king replied, "Because I wish I could make everything that I touch turn to gold."

"You shall have your wish", replied the stranger, and then he disappeared.

Next morning when the king was about to don his purple robe it became a cloth of gold. He sat down to fasten his sandals, and they became golden, too. He also saw that the chair in which he sat had turned to gold.

Now the king went in to breakfast, and as he lifted his goblet to drink, the liquid changed to gold and he could not drink it. Every morsel of food changed to a golden lump as he touched it. He realized that now he might starve to death.

His little daughter Marigold came running into the room and as she rushed to her father to kiss him, lo, she changed to a beautiful golden statue.

Then the king became very sorrowful and repentant of his rash wish, and he could not rest for remorse, "Alas, I am the most wretched man in the world", he cried, "Will no one lift this curse"?

At this the unknown visitor appeared before him, and said "Are you not happy, King Midas"? "Alas, I beg of you to take away this hateful gift", replied the king.

The stranger then told him to go to the nearby river and

to bathe in the stream, and the water would change his garments back to their original texture. King Midas lost no time in obeying, but as the water washed away the grains of gold, the river became golden, and it is said that the grains of gold sand have remained in the ocean to this day.

King Midas also sprinkled the water upon the golden objects in the palace and was overjoyed when his daughter came to life again. He became a happier king than he had even been before.

5.   The Legend of the Great Dipper.

There was once a great sorrow in the world. Everything seemed to be drying up; the people, the animals and every living thing suffered for thirst, and no water, dew, nor drop of moisture could they find.

A little child ran out into the night, carrying a small tin dipper, and prayed very earnestly for just that little cup of water. Suddenly she looked in the cup and found it filled to the brim with clear cold water, which would not spill, no matter how fast she ran home. As she ran she saw a little dog which seemed to be dying of thirst, so she poured a few drops in the palm of her hand and let the dog lap it. He immediately seemed to be much refreshed.

As the child went on the dipper became larger and larger, and filled with more water than before. She hurried on to bring the water to her mother, who took the dipper eagerly and was about to drink, when she saw that her servant was dying of thirst. So she passed the dipper of water to her lips and bade her drink. The servant revived and passed the dipper about the family until a stranger appeared, showing the same signs of thirst as themselves. The servant said. "Sacred are the needs of the stranger," and she pressed the dipper to the parched lips of the traveller.

Then a strange thing occurred. The dipper grew larger and larger and changed first from tin to silver, then to gold, and at length it seemed encrusted with diamonds which flashed in the sunlight, and inside the dipper a fountain gushed forth which supplied a thirsting nation as freely as it had supplied the needs of the little dog.

The stranger disappeared and a voice was heard chanting:— "Blessed is he that giveth a cup of water in My name."

Soon after the dipper was snatched up into the sky, where it has remained to flash and sparkle ever since. So, in northern lands, if you will look up into the sky, on any starry night, you may see the shining dipper, which is the token of unselfishness and kindly deeds.

Appendix. Teacher's Key.

Pp. 171-172. The teacher should ask the pupil to imitate the sounds made by the various animals indicated. She should observe the consonant and vowel sounds which are printed in the first column, opposite the name of the animal indicated.

Pp. 173-175. The teacher should try to have the child give the sounds listed by naming the objects seen in the pictures. These exercises may be *memorized* or *repeated after* the teacher, as the reading difficulties involved are too great for the pre-school child, or child in first and second grades. He may name the animals or objects seen in the pictures, and may give the sound made by the same.

Pp. 176-180. The words found on these pages appear in Thorndike's list of 2500 words in common use in the early grades, and in the Horn-Packer list of 5000 commonest words in the spoken vocabulary of children up to and including six years of age. A *few* sounds occur in only *one* of these lists. If the child *cannot read* the words, the teacher should have him *pronounce* them *after* her. The child may also use the words in sentences, after having pronounced them, as a check on spontaneous pronunciation.

Pp. 180-181. *Games in Phonics. Grades I and II.*

The teacher should speak the sentence and the child should give the answer, as indicated after each question, as "I growl and bark and follow my master. What am I?" *Answer.* "You are a *dog.*" The teacher may call upon every child in the room, insisting upon correct and clear answers. Each child who fails to give a satisfactory answer, must respond to several other questions made up by the children themselves, who may put the questions to the child, until he gives at least one clear-cut or satisfactory answer. It will stimulate children to speak more clearly, if the rivalry motive is used in this way.

If the black-board is used, the name of each child should appear, and a star should be given for each good answer. (i. e., from the standpoint of *good speech.*) Competition in the class is often a more satisfactory way of securing good speech from all children, than any other method. Children often *compete with each other* more satisfactorily than with adults.

Pp. 182-191. The exercises here are for use in grades I. and II. Pages may be read by the children for speech training and for accuracy of enunciation on the various vowel and consonant sounds. The fairy-tales and stories should be told by the teacher, and then retold by the pupils. The teacher should also ask the children to answer the questions given at the end of each story.

Grade III.

No. 1. For practise on l, m and n sounds.

No. 2. Long o and aw sounds. (well rounded tones).

No. 3. Short i and short o sounds. k sounds.

No. 4. Tw, tl, st and long i sounds.
No. 5. d, b, g, t sounds.
No. 6. gr, wh, w and short u sounds.
No. 7. p, ng,-ere (as in here) and -air (as in fair)
No. 8. b, f, pr, t, d, n, -ir, st sounds.

    j, n, ch, short oo (bush); ew (use); ow aloud.)

Grade IV.

No. I.	Line 1,	Fr. k, r, i
	Line 2,	ŭ, aw, ä
	Line 3,	ī, w, l,
	Line 4,	ă, ä, t
No. II	Line 5,	aw, ō, –ere.
	Line 6,	č, str
	Line 7,	pl, –air.
No. III	Line 1,	l, ŏŏ, ōō.
	Line 2,	sh, n, ng, th.
No. IV	Line 1,	aw, ŏ, ī, (igh)
	Line 2,	bl, –ir,
	Line 3,	ou, (around) a (pass)
	Line 4,	l, sk, kr, gr
	Line 5,	oh, w, bl, l,
	Line 6,	ng,
No. V	Line 1,	z, ng, b
	Line 2,	gz, y, ow
	Line 3,	gr.
No. VI	Line 1,	br, m, s, d,
	Line 2,	wh, n, th, s
	Line 3,	th, nd
No. VII	Line 1,	th, tr, st, nd
	Line 2,	pr,
	Line 3,	gr
	Line 4,	br
	Line 5,	pr, br
No. VIII	Line 1-4,	oh, m, aw, m, tl, ō
	Line 5,	w, ld, nk,
	Line 6,	l, n

Grade V.

No. I   Line 1,   gr, w,
             Line 2,   aw, ld,
             Line 3,   gr, br,
             Line 4,   nd, dr,

No. II   Line 1,   n, chr, wh, thr, h
             Line 2,   kr, st, m,
             Line 3,   ch, k
             Line 4,   th

No. III   Line 1,   s,
             Line 2,   sts, sh, ld,
             Line 3,   lz, lk, lv, shr
             Line 4,   sp.
             Line 5,   kl,
             Line 6,   thr,

No. IV   Line 1,   m, n, lz, sk
             Line 3,   tr,
             Line 4,   dr, lk,
             Line 6,   sl,
             Line 7,   gr, tl,
             Line 8,   sk, sp

No. V   Line 1,   p, b,
             Line 3,   m,

No. VI   Line 1,   k, j, sh (ocean)
             Line 2,   h, br, fr,
             Line 3,   shr, tr,
             Line 4,   th.

No. VII   Line 1-2,   wh, ō, ŏ
             Line 3,   g, f, thr
             Line 4,   h,

No. VIII   Line 1-2,   h, w, ō, ōō
             Line 3,   ch, chr.

Grade VI.

No. I.   Line 1,   w, l, tl, kr
              Line 2,   f, v

	Line 3,	gl,
	Line 4,	j,
	Line 5,	th, t
	Line 6,	th,
	Line 7,	th, sh,
	Line 8,	fl.
No. II.	Line 1,	w, m, ō, ou, (out)
	Line 2,	st, air,
	Line 3,	ch,
	Line 4,	l,
	Line 5,	vl,
No. III.	Line 1,	wh, ch, tr,
	Line 2,	sn,
	Line 4,	ch, l,
	Line 5,	sw,
	Line 6,	n, ng
No. IV.	Line 1,	m, n, nd
	Line 2,	ch, l, th
	Line 3,	spr, tl, ts
	Line 4,	wh, fr
No. V.	Line 1,	fl, l, r
	Line 2,	wh,
	Line 3,	bl, gr, kw, (quiver)
	Line 4,	sl, nks
	Line 6,	j,
	Line 7,	bl
	Line 8,	gr.

Grade VII.

No. 1. p. b. m.
No. 2. m, n.
No. 3. l sounds, initial, middle and final position.
No. 4. Initial and final k.
No. 5. Vowel sounds as in shield, guide, thee and us.
No. 6. t and d.

Grade VIII.

No. 1. n, ng, ch.
No. 2. l sounds.
No. 3. st, br, sl, gr and l sounds.
No. 4. p, b, m sounds.
No. 5. k and g.
No. 6. t, d and n.
No. 7. Retell story of the fox and the grapes, in your own words as directed.

Miscellaneous Graded and Ungraded Exercises.

Grades 1–4 inclusive. Fables 1, 2, 3, 4 and 5. Have the child read the story aloud, or divide the reading among the children in the class; ask someone to retell the story.

2. The teacher may read or tell the story to the class, and then ask various pupils to participate in answering, or the children may prompt the speaker if he errs on certain parts of the story.

3. In the fables, ask the children to tell what lessons they teach.

4. Ask the children to tell short stories or fables which they know. Use this exercise as a basis for distinct speech.

5. Have the child stand and face the class in telling the story; be sure that he stands in good poise, and do not accept anything less than *the best* the speaker is able to do, in his telling of the story.

Easy Sentences. Grades III to V.

The sounds to be observed are as follows:—
Sentence 1. Initial and middle h (*h*orse un*h*arness)
Sentence 2. Initial, middle and final f.
Sentence 3. Initial, middle and final v.
Sentence 4. Initial, middle and final p.
Sentence 5. Initial, middle and final b. (*b*ear, ru*bb*ing, cri*b*)
Sentence 6. Initial, middle and final m.
Sentence 7. Initial, middle and final t (*T*om, bu*tt*on, coa*t*).
Sentence 8. Initial, middle and final d (*d*eed, ri*dd*le, Te*d*).

Sentence 9. Initial, middle and final n (*n*ow, di*nn*er, noo*n*).

Sentence 10. Initial, middle and final k (*k*itty, bas*k*et, noo*k*).

Sentence 11. Initial, middle and final g (*g*reat, a*g*o, ru*g*).

Sentence 12. Middle and final ng. (si*ng*ing; so*ng*.)

Sentence 13. Initial, middle and final ch (*ch*ild, scrat*ch*ing,
match.)

Sentence 14. Initial, middle and final j (*J*ennie, en*j*oys, fu*dg*e).

Sentence 15. Initial, middle and final s (*s*aw, si*s*ter, thi*s*).

Sentence 16. Initial, middle and final z (*z*ero, ob*s*erved,
freeze.)

Sentence 17. Initial, middle and final sh. (*sh*e, wa*sh*ing, di*sh*).

Sentence 18. –ew (ju) as in new; and zh in middle position, as
(as in mea*s*ure.)

Sentence 19. w and wh (as in Will and wheel).

Sentence 20. l (*l*adder, pu*l*led, wa*ll*.)　　　..

Sentence 21. r (as in *r*at, me*rr*y.)

Sentence 22. y (*y*ellow).

Sentence 23. x (ks) (as in the *eks* and the *egs* sounds).

Sentence 24. kw (as in *qu*een and ac*qu*ainted).

Sentence 25. br, tr.

Sentence 26. bl, tl (lit*tl*e).

Sentence 27. spr, pt.

Miscellaneous Exercises, Grades V to VIII.

1. Read the fables and folk tales and retell them in your
    own words.
2. Answer the questions about the Legends of the Days and
    Hours and tell the story of the Seasons in your own words.
3. Tell the story of the *Three Wishes in* your own words.
4. Tell the story called *Diamonds and Toads.* Can you apply
    this story to Speech in any way.
5. Retell the story *The Golden Touch.*
6. Tell the Legend of *The Great Dipper* in your own words.

Exercises and Tests For the Pre-School Child;
Exercises for Grades I to VIII

THE most helpful method in dealing with a speech defect is to analyze the difficulty at the outset of the disturbance and to apply corrective or therapeutic measures immediately, if possible, according to the nature
of the difficulty. Parents, teachers and friends need to
be especially patient and persistent in dealing with a
child having speech defects. Nagging, scolding and
sharp words only intensify the maladjustment and
plunge the child deeper into the Slough of Despond.
Correctness in utterance, care in enunciation, observ-
ance of *how* the sounds are made are some of the ways
in which an adult may help a child. It is generally
agreed that no one "method" will apply to all cases,
and for this reason many workers in the field of speech
object to outlining a "method", as they say it must be
flexible and varied to suit the needs of the individual
child. There are, however, some simple hygienic and
physical measures that are useful in treating many
children who have speech disturbances. While the exercises here given are not all inclusive, and make no
claim to completeness, so far as any particular "system" is concerned, they illustrate some general principles which have been found useful in the experience
of the writer in dealing with a large number of cases
of speech defect with children in Pennsylvania, Massachusetts, Iowa and Wisconsin. Many of the exercises
are only suggestive and need to be supplemented with
additional material, but there are many good texts on
the market which offer special training in intensive
phonetic methods, letter and sound training, exercises
in articulation, and the like. These exercises are in-

tended to offer a somewhat comprehensive outline for speech therapy for use among teachers of speech, and especially for those working in the field of speech correction.

Among methods mentioned by various writers one finds the following suggestions.

1. Strengthen the will by a change in speech tempo.

Breathing.

2. Writers are divided as to the use of breathing exercises. Many agree that they are to be used in cases other than stuttering, but never in the case of the stutterer, except through simple gymnastic and posture exercises in such a way that attention is not focussed upon breathing.
3. Vocal and articulatory exercises.
4. Use of International Phonetic Symbols, in whatever language.
5. Medical treatment when necessary or advisable.
6. Intelligence tests to determine the mental level.
7. A thorough physical examination.
8. A careful case-history study of the patient.
9. Committing to memory short passages.
10. Reading aloud at frequent intervals.
11. Reading and retelling short stories and events.
12. Spontaneous conversations.
13. Reading of dialogues in which one part is read by the teacher.
14. Learning to speak slowly and calmly.
15. Placing the emphasis upon the vowel quality in the word, and learning that consonant sounds are relatively "noisy" and unimportant. Much emphasis should be upon the vowel element, as it is the backbone of the word and the most important element. At the same time, the consonants must be sounded and lightly included in saying the word or phrase.
16. The radio broadcaster speaks slowly and distinctly. The

child should be taught to think of himself as a broadcaster, or as recording for the phonograph, speaking
slowly and distinctly in order that he may make a good
"record". Slovenly speech sounds do not make a clear
record, nor do they fall pleasantly on the ear of the
listener.

17. The child should read and retell short stories and news-
paper clippings or current events.

18. The child should read poems each day to someone at
home and also to the teacher; he should retell the contents to some member of the family.

19. Encourage the child to ask questions. Have him also ask
questions and answer them himself.

20. Let the child call off names of railroad stations through
a megaphone.

21. Have him tell a joke or humorous story to the teacher.

22. Have him read headlines from the paper or magazine
and discuss the article therein mentioned.

23. Let the child pretend to be a salesman selling goods to a
customer. Let the roles be reversed. Also have him apply
to an imaginary official for a position of some kind.

24. Have him hold an imaginary telephone conversation with
some one.

25. Let him enact the part of a railroad ticket agent selling
you a ticket to some distant point. Then reverse the roles.

26. Have him introduce himself to you. Have him ask if you
are waiting for someone and if he may help you to locate
the person.

27. Prepare a short speech on radio, bicycling, automobiling,
boy scout activities, girl scout activities, and tell it to the
teacher.

28. Have the child practise posture exercises and deep breathing, so that he may stand well, and speak in a relaxed,
easy manner, when called upon to recite in school. Have
him take time to think, to relax, and to speak slowly.
There is no merit in hurried speech. "Do not regard
hurry as a necessary part of modern life."

While the above suggestions are especially useful in dealing with the stutterer they furnish an outline for several weeks' work which may be profitably employed in any type of speech correction work, although they need to be supplemented in case they are used with lispers or others where phonetic drills and letter substitution need to be included.

I. *Relaxation Exercises.*

1. Stand in good poise, head up, chest high, hips well back, knees straight.
2. Head flexion exercises, bending right and left in 4 counts.
3. Same bending head forward and back in 4 counts.
4. Head rotation, left and right in 4 counts.
5. Arm extension, right and left.
    Extend arms forward from position "upward bend"!
    "   "   overhead   "   "   "   "
    "   "   backward   "   "   "   "
6. Shoulder-blade movement.
    Make a large circle in front of the face by swinging the arm freely (as in swinging Indian Clubs). First with right arm; then with left arm.
7. Repeat at sides.
8. Repeat in front, using both arms. (Do not bend arms at elbow, during the swing, but pivot from shoulder with full, free-arm swing.)
9. Hips firm! Trunk rotation, left and right (keeping lower limbs stationary, rotate upper portion of body, i. e., the trunk, from the waist line, describing a large circle with this part of your body.
10. Trunk flexion, bend forward and up to original position, 2 counts.
11. Trunk flexion, to side, first left then right, in 4 counts.
12. Trunk backward bend, (slightly, only) and then back to original position in 2 counts. Following this, bend forward and downward and back to position, in 2 counts.

Note: Dr. S. S. Curry's fundamental laws which appear in his book, "The Foundations of Expression," include some of the following excellent speech maxims:—

1. Action precedes, determines, and supports speech.
2. Pantomime, by means of the sign language, was the first form of communication. Speech and patois developed at a later biological period. (We appear sometimes to have forgotten all about the gesture language!)
3. Natural training must follow nature's method, i. e., the physical law of evolution. Speech follows as the outward manifestation of the inward processes.
4. The instrument (the body) must be attuned (*trained*) before melody (*speech and song*) may be secured.

II. *Respiratory Exercises and Tone Production.*

An outline for exercises to be used in speech training, (see footnote on page 225).

1. Standing in an erect position, raise arms overhead, side-wise and upward as you breathe in. Lower the arms as you breathe out. Same as I count, 1-2; (raise on 1, lower on 2.) Count 10 times.
2. Same, raising arms forward and upward. Breathe in and out as I count, 1-2, 1-2, 1-2, (5 times).
3. Feet apart, neck firm, trunk sideways bend, left and right in 4 counts. Ready! 1, 2, 3, 4! Repeat. 1, 2, 3, 4! Again, breathing in on the upward trunk movement, 1, 2, 3, 4!
4. Neck firm, chest expanded, trunk forward bend! (with head high). Upward stretch! Same in 2 counts, 1-2! Repeat, 1-2! (5 times).
5. With one hand on upper chest and other at pit of stomach, note the expansion as you breathe in. Notice the enlarging of the lower chest region as you breathe in and the shrinkage as you breathe out. Breathe in while I count to five, ready! 1, 2, 3, 4, 5! Hold 1, 2, 3, 4, 5! Breathe out as I count 1, 2, 3, 4, 5. Repeat 5 Times.
6. Same as the above as I count 8. Same to 10 counts.

7. Breathe in as I count 5, and let the breath go out slowly as you hiss "SSSSSSSS!" (Hiss and prolong the sound as long as outgoing breath lasts).

8. Same, chanting the word "Home", as you breathe out, prolonging the MMMMMMMMMMM sound.

9. Same chanting AH, and prolonging as long as breath is going out.

10. Same whispering "Yes", and prolonging the *s* as long as possible on one breath.

11. Same, chanting "Oh" and prolonging as above.

12. Same Chanting OO and prolonging.

13. Count to 20 in groups of 4, as, 1, 2, 3, 4; 5, 6, 7, 8; etc.

Note: In dealing with stutterers attention *should not be called to the mechanics of breathing,* and the muscles concerned, because calling attention to any reflex mechanisms, such as breathing, may interfere with the coördination of the muscles and thus increase the difficulty, particularly in the case of the stutterer. In such cases posture, deep breathing and breath control must be gained by indirection, or by allowing the pupil to follow the movements of the teacher without directing attention to the muscles involved.

III. *Speech Hygiene Program, for Daily Practise.**

(For the Patient.)

I. Regular hours of sleep, nine hours or more per night. Retire at 8:30, if you are less than eighteen years old,—an hour later, as a customary thing, if you are older.

II. Try to go to sleep immediately with pleasant, cheerful thoughts. The easiest way to accomplish this is to relax as completely as possible, and seek to become "drowsy."

III. Try not to become very much excited when you are talking. Cultivate habits of calm, easy speech, free from hesitation, "noises" and nervous mannerisms.

IV. Say to yourself, "I am not afraid; I know that I can

* All of the above directions apply to practically all speech students, but 13 and 14 are intended particularly for those who stutter.

make all the sounds in the English language. I will try to speak them easily and well."

V. Use pleasant, agreeable tones. Try to get out of a jerky, unrhythmic monotone in speech, if such is your usual way of speaking.

VI. Eat plenty of fruits and green, leafy vegetables when they can be secured. Avoid eating sweets to excess. Do not spend your allowance for candy.

VII. Eat slowly and masticate your food thoroughly.

VIII. Exercise at least two hours each day out of doors.

IX. Keep a cheerful, pleasant attitude all the time.

X. Don't worry about your speech. It is worry which sends it off into a jerky, unpleasant utterance. Calmness and control of yourself whenever you begin to speak will give you easy, fluent utterance if you practise it often enough.

XI. Remember that it will take time to improve, but begin NOW to relax, and make up your mind that you are going to conquer your speech habits rather than allow them to master YOU!

XII. Read "The Americanization of Edward W. Bok", and like him seek every possible occasion to improve yourself, to talk with interesting people, to take upon yourself some of the responsibility for social occasions and thus direct the development of your own personality.

XIII. Remember that for some time, an occasional hesitation is to be expected if you have stuttered for a good many years,—but *stop* the moment hesitation or jerky speech occurs and get a new grip on yourself; make a new and better start, without facial contortions, grimaces and "tied-up" muscle movements of head and shoulders. Be a self-starter of the mental typ ; don't let your hands and feet start the performance!

XIV. Relax, relax, RELAX! Speech should be easy and spontaneous. Occasionally call some of your friends on the telephone, or answer the calls whenever possible, until you can do this successfully. Boys and girls who stutter often have a strange fear of the telephone. Overcome this fear, realizing that it is easier to talk to some people over the telephone than in the same room.

XV. Do not depend on some other member of your family to talk for you, thus assuming the social responsibility which should be partly yours. Be gracious and tactful enough to do your share, and try to do it easily and well. Self-consciousness is the bug-bear which most often makes us appear awkward and ill-at-ease.

IV. *Speech Hygiene Program for the Family.*

I. Fathers and Mothers,—cultivate calm, easy speech in your home, and demand it from every member of your family. Avoid nervous haste and excitement in talking. Seek to be reasonably deliberate in speech and to serve to your sons and daughters as a constant model of natural, gracious, easy speech.

II. Quietly suggest that each child talk slowly and clearly at home.

III. Encourage the child to talk, find things of interest for him to talk about, but insist upon good speech from the very start.

IV. Distinctness of utterance, careful manners, quiet, self-assured speech are to be held up to the child as ear-marks of good breeding.

V. Insist upon good manners in little things, as the child passes out of the five year old period,—teaching him to wait upon you, to place at the table your chair or that of a guest, to allow you to precede, in entering a room; show him that you want him to do credit to himself and the family, in a social way, at home and abroad.

VI. If a child hesitates or "blocks off" in speech, or tries to talk too rapidly, stop him *quietly,* and ask him to begin again. Have him stop AT ONCE; do not let the stutter habit gain a foothold, if you can help it. Do not let him speak on an incoming breath; he should breathe in slowly and then speak on the outgoing breath.

VII. Help the child to overcome the "stoop-shoulder" habit. Cultivate erect bearing, obey the *Posture Rules* like good soldiers. Remember that we should carry the head erect, chest expanded, knees straight (not sagging in indolent fashion) and hips well back. Do not let the child sit for hours curled up in a chair, bending over a book. He can sit properly if required to do so.

VIII. Help children to cultivate calm, cheerful dispositions, free from whining, nervousness, worry or mental strain.

IX. Practice bodily exercises and simple gymnastics each day.

1. Arm stretching exercises.

2. Head rotations, bending and flexions.

3. Freedom of shoulders (in arm movements).

4. Breathing exercises (without directing attention to the ACT of Breathing or the muscles concerned!) Get at it indirectly through counting, phrasing, sentence building, etc. Work for smooth, easy responses, counting in groups of numbers, five counts on one breath. In this manner, count from 1 to 5, then 5-10; 10-15; 15-20; and 20-25.

Count to 50 in groups of 10 (10 to each breath).

Count to 45 in groups of 15.

Say the alphabet on one breath.

Read some short poem, being sure that you take a new breath for each line. If this is too difficult, take a new breath for each phrase, speaking slowly and distinctly.

V. *Daily Menu.*

Monday, Tues.   Wed., Thurs.   Friday, Saturday, Sunday
Good Food   A Calm Spirit   Plenty of the Right Food
                Plenty of Good Cheer
A Varied Program   Milk, Greens, Fruit
        Judicious forgetfulness of one's ailments.
        Forgetfulness of self.   Appreciation.
        Consideration for the Other Fellow.
Politeness.   Helpfulness.
        A little accurate knowledge.
Good Books.   Out-of-door-games.
        A determination to Be Like Folks.
Relaxation   DAILY REST   DAILY EXERCISE
                DAILY PRACTICE.
Home Obligations.   Belief in YOURSELF.

Recipes.

You will find that Luck is only the Pluck
   To try things over and over.
Patience and skill, courage and will
   Are the four leaves of Lucky Clover.

Did you tackle that trouble that came your way,
   With a resolute heart and cheerful?
Or hide your face from the light of day
   With a craven soul, and fearful?
Oh, a trouble's a ton, or a trouble's an ounce,
   Or a trouble is What You Make It!
It isn't the fact that you're licked that counts.
   But only HOW did you TAKE it?

You are beaten to earth? Well, well, what's that?
   Come up with a smiling face.
It isn't the fact that you're down that counts,
   But to lie there, that's the disgrace.

                  E. Vance Cook.

VI. *Exercises for Agility of Tongue.*

(May be used in All Grades.)

1. lah, lay, lee, –lah, lay, lee, –lah, lay, lee –lah.
2. Tah, tay, tee, –tah, tay, tee,– tah, tay, tee, tah.
3. Same with dah, day, dee, etc.-----------
4. Same with rah, ray, ree, etc.-----------
5. Same with nah, nay, nee, etc.-----------
6. kah, kay, kee, etc. --------------------
7. gah, gay, gee, etc. --------------------
8. chah, chay, chee,-------chah, chay, chee, –chah, chay, chee, –chah
9. jah, jay, jee. ----------------------

10.　sar, say, see. ----------------------
11.　zar, zay, zee, ---------------------
12.　shar, shay, shee. --------------------
13.　zhah, zhay, zhee. --------------------
14.　fah, fay, fee. ---------------------
15.　vah, vay, vee ----------------------
16.　yah, yay, yee. --------------------
17.　wah, way, wee. --------------------
18.　whah, whay, whee. ------------------
19.　pah, pay, pee, pah, pay, pee, pah, pay, pee, pah.
20.　bah, bay, bee, –bay, bay, bee, –bay, bay, bee– bah.
21.　mah, may, mee, etc.-----------------

VII. *Exercises for Relaxation of Jaw.*

1. "Relax jaw, opening mouth as in a sleepy yawn. Open as I count one, and close on two, Ready! 1 - 2, 1 - 2," etc. (count ten times.)

2. Agility of tongue exercise.

"This time we are going to clean house. I want you to sweep the roof of your mouth with your tongue. Begin at the front close to your teeth, and let your tongue sweep along the roof of your mouth, till it goes back as far as it can, and touches the highest point in your mouth! Already, 1 - 2" (Sweep on one, relax tongue and bring it back to floor of the mouth, on two.)

3. "This time I want to dot the roof of your mouth with your tongue three times, once at the front as I say 1, farther back as I say 2, and way back as I say 3. Ready, begin. 1, 2, 3, Relax!"

4. "This time I want to see how far you can extend your tongue forward. Already, out, - in!" Try five times.

5. "This time let your tongue relax and lay in floor of the mouth and open mouth as in a yawn. Ready, open, close!" (5 times.)

VIII. *Gymnastics for Speech Muscles.*

I.

A. *Lips and jaw.*
1. Oo, ah, ee, ah, oo. –oo, ee, ah;
   Ee, oo, ah, – – – – – –ah, oo, ee.
2. Ah, ay, ee, aw, oh, oo; ōō, ŏŏ, ōh, aw, ŏ, äh.
3. Lah, lay, lee, law, loh, loo.
4. Pull upper lip down between lower teeth.
5. Bite lower lip lightly with upper teeth.
6. Alternate first upper and then lower lip.
7. Relax as in yawn, to count 1 (open) 2 (close).
8. Side to side, in two counts. (jaw movement).
9. Extend jaw forward and then relax (2 counts).

II.

B. *Tongue exercise using mirror.*
1. Thin and flatten the tongue.
2. Thicken and round tongue.
3. Extend forward with pointed tip.
4. Extend downward toward jaw.
5. Extend up toward tip of nose.
6. Side to side; dot corners of mouth.
7. Sweep roof of mouth.
8. Dot roof of mouth.
9. Tongue from right side of cheek to left side.

III.

C. *Relaxation and invigoration of soft palate.*
1. ah–ung–ah; ah, ong, ah; ee–ung–ee; ay, ung, ay.
2. ah–hung, ah; ay, hang, ay; ee, hung, ee;
3. oh, hung, oh; oo, ung, oo. i, hung, i
4. ah, sah; ah, sah; ah, sah.
5. ah, gar; ah, gar; ah, gar, etc.

IV.

D. *Breathing exercises.*
1. Stand with chest expanded, head erect, hips well back, knees with sufficient muscle tonus to give good poise.

Breathe in, in 2 counts. Hold two counts, release in two counts.

2. Same in 4 counts. Same in 6 counts.

3. Slow intake of breath, rapid outgo in whispers, "yes" (prolonging the hissing sound, as long as breath is easily controlled) whisper on outgoing breath, of course.)

4. Deep breath. Pronounce word HOME, on 1 count prolonging the humming sound as long as you can easily.

5. Rapid inhalation and slow outgoing breath, counting to 20 in groups of five, as 1, 2, 3, 4, 5, (Breath) 6, 7, 8, 9, 10, etc.

IX. *Exercises for Speech Agility.*

(The following sentences are not intended for drill or practise other than to serve as an occasional measure of muscle coördination and gain in skill in the use of the muscles involved in speech, as they are a mild indication of speech agility, rapidity of thought processes and flexibility in the mechanics of speech.)

I. Bi-labials. Wh, W. B. P. M. Phonetic symbols; hw, w, b, p, m.

1. Paul, the popular Pope, appointed Potipher to protect the public parks.

2. Blundering Brown, the big blusterer, bragged brazenly about his bad brother.

3. The enemy's mules mutilated many mained militiamen.

4. The wind is west and the waves are wild.

5. The wherry at the wharf was laden with wheat and whale-oil.

II. Labio-dentals. F, V. Phonetic symbols, f. v.

6. Phillip fought his way forward toward the ferry.

7. Vivian's vocabulary gives evidence of vitality and vigor.

III. Lingua-dentals. Th (voiced) and th (voiceless). Symbols. ð, ө.

8. Through thin cloth the thorns were thrust.

9. The brothers were gathering heather together.

IV. Lingua-rugal. S. Z. Sh, Zh, L. T. D. Ch J. Phonetic symbols:—s, z, ʃ, ʒ, l, t, d, tʃ, dʒ.

10. After a stormy session Saul listened to the songs.

11. The sounds of the zither resounded through prison walls.

12. She ṣaw the ship, a shining shape upon a shimmering sea.

13. With measured tread they bore the treasure to the pleasure dome.

14. Look before you leap, and let your judgment lead, usually.

15. Tom treated the matter tactfully, tenderly and truthfully.

16. The date recorded did not agree with Dan's desk memorandum.

17. The brook chatters cheerfully as it flows to join the joyous river.

V. Lingua-palatal. Y. R. Phonetic symbols, j. r.

18. You see yon yellow yacht in yonder bay?

19. Round the rough crag ran the ragged, merry, rollicker.

VI. Lingua-velar. K. G. Symbols. k, g.

20. The Klux Klan kept a keen watch over Caleb Keith.

21. Grumbling ungraciously he gave a gloomy greeting.

VII. Glottal aspirate. H. Hu, symbols, h, hj.

22. How could Henry hear of her happy fate?

23. Hugo knew the heroic traits of humanity.

VIII. Nasal resonants. M, N, Ng. Symbols, m, n, ŋ.

24. My mother made me my new muffler.

25. Neither you nor I need notice Ned's nervousness.

26. Rising and leaping, curling and creeping, singing and swinging, it swings on its way.

X. *Exercises for Pitch Variations and Modulations of Voice.*

Practise these sentences with good variations of tone and inflection.

1. Rich gifts wax poor, when givers prove unkind.

2. What is it that gentlemen wish? What would they have?

3. Shall we try argument? Shall we resort to force and entreaty?

4. We shall *not* fail. We are not *weak*.

5. The war is inevitable, let it come. I repeat, sirs, let it come!

6. I have no way of judging the future, but by the past.

7. Say the following in several different ways, as:—

a. (a statement of fact.) He is a worthy gentleman.

b. Emphasize the pronoun.

c. Emphasize the noun.

d. Dispute someone who denies it.

e. Define the kind of man he is.

f. Question or doubt it.

g. Sarcasm or irony.

8. Same with these sentences. He will go, will he?

9. John did not buy that house.

10. Ah, I am delighted. This is remarkable.

11. Hath a dog money? Is it possible a cur can lend three thousand ducats?

12. I maintained that every man should have his own ideals.

13. Are you going up town?

14. Practice the following sentences with mirror, watching the changing position of tongue on the different vowel sounds:—(Front vowels, ēē, ĭ, ĕh, air, ă, I, äh. As in "He is met there at my father's." First try sentence, then the vowels alone.*

15. Who would go call on father? ōō, ŏŏ, ō, aw, ŏ, äh.

16. Words about us. (ur, ə, uh.)

17. Inflect these words; union, liberty; nation, American, awake, singing, bringing, standard, constitution, tonight, tomorrow, arise, come here, come home, oh no, today singing, hanging, clanging, good-evening, yesterday.

Sing from high to low (coming down scale,) Follow, follow, follow, follow, follow, follow me. Sing first words and say last ones, gradually increasing the number of words spoken, until entire phrase is spoken instead of being sung.

*See Daggett. Windsor; Phonographic Lesson Series. N. Y. C.

XI. *Word Drill.*

A. Practise the following consonants in initial, middle and final position, in these words.

Phonetic Training.

Consonant Sounds.	Key Words.
1. p	pay– ripple– wrap
2. b.	bay –ribbon – rub
3. m	may – rumble –room
4. t	tie – whittle – fit
5. d.	dough – riddle – bud
6. n	no – under – run
7. k	king – wrinkle – stick
8. g	gun – baggage – rug
9. ng	–––– ringing – sing
10. f	free – offer – off
11. v	view – over – cove, of
12. ch	child – fetching – pitch
13. j	jury – enjoy – judge
14. s	say – master – miss
15. z	zero – busy – buzz
16. sh	show – bushel – rash
17. zh	–––– azure – rouge, garage.
18. *th* (voiced)	this – whither– bathe.
19. (th) (voiceless)	thin, birthday, month.
20. l	look willing – bill
21. r	rat, merit,
22. er, ir,	about, energy, brother, prayer (in un-accented syllables).
23. ur, ir,	err, myrrh, mermaid, bird, (accented syllables).
24. h	hat, unhand.
25. y	you, yellow, yes
26. hu	hue, huge, Hugh, Hugo, human
27. w	war, unwind (unwaind)
28. wh (hw)	what, where,

B. *Vowel Sounds*. Practise these words giving special attention to making the vowel distinct.

ä	arm, father
ī	fly, high, (flai, hai)
ă	hat, map.
ŭ	up, cup
u, ōō,	food, June
u, ŏŏ,	foot, put
ĕ	get, met
ē	ee, we
ā	day, cake (dei, keik)
aîr, câre,	chair, fare, heir, hair
ir, ur	b*urr,* le*a*rn
ä	*a*gain, absolute, *another.*
ĭ	it, sit
ō	go, row
ŏ	not, lot doll
ȯ	November
aw, au	law, water
oy, oi,	toy, joy
ear,	fear, here
ire,	fire, hire.

Phonetics

XII. *Practise Words and Sentences.*

1. e as in wē.
   Be, see, seat, beef, receive, meet, thief.
   The thief received his freedom, last evening.
2. Short i as in ĭt.
   It, bit, dipper, hit, whip, quick, busy, happy, is.
   It is a pity that he is not happy.
   There was a din in the city.
3. Short e as in mĕt.
   Bread, said, many, very, pleasure, measure.
   A trench extended to the French lines.
4. Short a as in măn.

Man, plan, cat, Manchester, catch, happy.

Catch this packet of matches, Jack.

5. a as in äsk.

After, ask, demand, pass, grass, dance.

The commander advanced along the pathway.

6. Italian *a* as in fäther.

Palm, psalm, half, calm, aunt, hard, card.

My aunt will depart this afternoon.

7. Short o as in nŏt.

Lost, not, sod, God, was, top, Boston.

The frog sat on a log in the bog.

8. Sound of aw as in law.

Water, law, saw, all, sort, lord, also.

His daughter crossed the lawn at his call.

9. O (in unaccented syllables) as in ōbey.

Obey, Ohio, obedience, November, disobey.

The poet wrote a poem about November.

10. U (or o͝o) as in bo͝ok.

Foot, cook, put, soot, hook, took, pulley.

Put the cushion in that nook.

11. U or ōo as in mōon.

Do, rule, cool, mood, blue, noon, shoe.

Who goes to school in the afternoon?

She crooned two negro songs.

12. U as in cŭp.

Flood, mud, dove, sup, blush, butter.

Flushed with success he brushed them aside.

13. Er, ir, or ur in accented syllables.

Fern, burr, murmur, pearl, bird, earl, myrrh.

The earl murmured a work to the colonel.

14. The indefinite, or sound of a, er, u, etc. in unaccented syllables.

Again, alike, about, China, mother, venture.

15. A as in dāy.

May, chain, say, data, strata, gratis.

Did you say he might come today?

16. Ere or air as in chair and there.

Share, care, mare, heir, there, fare.

Her fair brow is wrinkled with care.

17. I as in whīte.

Light, sight, crisis, library, bribe, buy.

The wise wife tried to hide the knife.

18. Ew or u as in few or tune.

Youth, view, news, tune, due, use, pure.

The Union troops will march Tuesday.

19. O as in gō.

No, blow, stone, roll, flow, old, rose.

A rolling stone gathers no moss.

He spoke about an ancient oak tree.

20. Oy as in boy.

Joy, toy, annoy, coil, noisy, foil, soil.

Roy is a noisy boy with his toys.

21. Ow as in cow.

Vow, mount, gown, crown, count, bough.

They found the count near the mountain.

22. Our as in hour and tower.

Power, tower, bower, flower, hour.

The shower will refresh the flowers.

23. Ire as in fire and tire.

Fire, mire, higher, tire, buyer, ire, crier.

The fire began to mount higher and higher.

24. Oor, as in poor.

Poor, tour, moor, doer, cure, renewer.

He was too poor to take a long tour.

XIII. *Word Drill.*

1.	ah.	parl,	barl,	larb	marl.
2.	ay	paid, bale, labe, male.			
3.	ee	peel, beel, leeb, meel.			
4.	aw	pall, bawl, lawb, mawl.			
5.	oh	pole, bole, lobe, mole.			
6.	oo	pool, bool, loob, mool.			
7.	i	pile, bile, libe, mile.			

8.	e	pet, bet, led, mel.
9.	air	pair, bare, lair, fair.
10.	er, a	about, alike, again, ado, prayer.
11.	ir, ur	pearl, bird, learn, myrrh.
12.	i	pit, bit, limb, mit.
13.	ear	peer, beer, leer, meer.
14.	ire	pyre, byer, lyre, mire.
15.	ow	pout, bout, lout, rout.
16.	oi, oy	boil, foil, loin, soil.
17.	u, oo	pull, full, bush, foot.
18.	u	pun, bun, punt, lull.
19.	ew	your, view, beauty, due, new, duke.
20.	a	pan, mat, lam, lap.
21.	o	pom, pol, lot, lom.

Directions: The above exercises may be used for training in voice placing, tone production and intonation. They may be used to improve the range of tone, through rising and falling inflections, alternating first the rising and then falling tone. They are also intended for practise on purity of vowel quality. The vowels are used with consonants made well forward in the mouth and therefore the tone is projected, or made well forward, and pupil is less likely to produce throaty, nasal tones than when the vowels are used with mid or back consonants.

XIV. *Voice, Exercises.*

Practise with open, melodious tones to improve vowel quality.

I.   Chant on one note.   OO, OO, OO, OO, OO (long)
                            AH, AH, AH, AH, AH
                            AY, AY, AY, AY, AY
                            EE, EE, EE, EE, EE
                            OO, OO, OO, OO, OO (short)

II.   Say with rising and falling pitch,
                            pool, poor, loom, loot
                            pull, full, book, cook
                            pole, mole, loan, roan
                            pet, let, bet, met

pine, line, mine, dine
pin, fin, lit, tin
pale, male, late, bale
art, hard, mart, lard
lawn, law, saw, paw
pair, lair, mare, fare
pan, man, pall, mall
par, mar, lark, marl
peel, beel, seal, meal

		2, 3, 4, 5?			3, 4, 5?
(Ask)	1.		Ask.	1, 2,	
Ans.	1,		Ans.	1, 2,	
		2, 3, 4, 5!			3, 4, 5.
		4, 5?	Ans.	1, 2, 3,	
Ask.	1, 2, 3,				4, 5.
		5.	Ans.	1, 2, 3, 4,	
Ask.	1, 2, 3, 4,				5.

III. Who killed Cock Robin? "I" said the sparrow.
"With my little arrow. I killed Cock Robin."

IV. "Who dares!" This was the patriot's cry,
As striding from his desk he came,
"Come out with me in freedom's name.
For her to live, for her to die!"
A hundred hands flung up reply.
A hundred voices shouted, "I"!

XV. Sentences for Practise on Consonant Combinations.

A.

1. pr.   He praised the preacher.
2. br.   The braid was brought from Paris.
3. fr.   The frost ruined the fruit.
4. thr. We thrill as we hear the notes from the throat of the thrush.
5. dr.   In his dream he was at drill.
6. kr.   The deer crashed thru the creek.
7. gr.   The dog growled his greeting.

8. sp.   With spike and spade he speeded along.
9. sm.   The smoke makes my eyes smart.
10. st.   They stopped, being stunned by the noise.
11. sn.   The snail has a snug little house.
12. sk.   With skill he guided the skiff.
13. sw.   Swiftly gathered the swarm.
14. skw.   The squire heard the pig squeal.
15. sk.   The husky farm lad came at dusk.
16. spl.   As the ice split, he went in with a splash.
17. spr.   The sprite danced in the spray.
18. shr.   The shrewd man never once shrank from the task.
19. skr.   The scribe opened the scroll.

B. *Exercise Practise on Vowels and Prefixes.*

1. The exact date is not known.
2. He escaped the unwelcome employment.
3. The child kept the empty box.
4. They robed him in a blanket which had been warmed at the fireside.
5. The object is to overtake the runner.
6. She was unable to undergo the ordeal.
7. The company gave a command to collect the tickets from the corrupt conductor.
8. Iowa prefers to produce much wheat when she perceives that she can foretell a rapid sale.
9. Before you decide to remove to a new place, select the kind of work which you can best do.

C. *Wyllie Sentence for Speech Drill, on Consonant Sounds.*

1. Peter Brown made white wax.
2. A few fine villages.
3. Thinkest thou so?
4. Behold Great Zeus.
5. She leisurely took down nine large red roses.
6. Can Gilbert bring home yeast?

D. *Sentence Drill.*

1. Patty, bring more white wafers.
2. I think this will do.

3. I saw a few fine vines in the vineyard.
4. Does Zeus answer the people thus?
5. She tried to drill nine youths.
6. George can blow the bugler's horn.
7. Ring the library bell, please.

Sentence Drill.

1. p.   Peter was picking the peppers.
2. m.   Mother, make more mince meat.
         Mother make me my new coat.
3. n.   No, no, not now.
         There is nothing new under the sun.
4. b.   Billy Barton bought a biscuit.
         Betty bought some butter.
5. d.   Davy dreamt he saw a dragon.
6. g.   Gaffer Gray got a goose and a gander.
7. t.   The tall timbers cover two lots.
8. k, kw. Come quickly, the cows are in the corn.
9. v.   Verily, he has saved enough.
10. ng.   He sits and sings his cheery song.

XVI. *Word Discrimination.*

Upper Grades or High School. Select the Slang Phrases.
1. Certainly I expect to be present.
2. I will be there sure thing.
3. Please tell Mabel to hustle up.
4. William expects to make good in his new position.
5. Please hurry to the store.
6. The singer did not make a hit.
7. Oh go on, that's no way to do.
8. Did you catch on to what they meant?
9. Will you come on, now?
10. It's a cinch he didn't mean to do that.
11. He made a motion that the meeting adjourn.
12. You'll have to get a move on, if you catch that train.
13. I had an awful good time.
14. Isn't that just great of her!

15. This is the most elegant room I've ever seen.
16. I think she's quite a peach.
17. I don't like her, she's such a mess.
18. The commandant reprimanded the sailor at mess.
19. Company A was urged to carry on.
20. I never saw such carryings-on.
21. Give me the what-do-you-call-it.
22. A good book? I'll say it is!
23. Shall I go now? Not on your life.
24. Give me a pinch of salt.
25. I call that all stuff and nonsense!
26. You bet I intend to go.
27. I'll tell the world there's some class to him.
28. For my sweet sake, I bid you seek it not.
29. For the love of Mike, do not do that.
30. After such an act, he was decidedly in the soup.
31. Isn't that gown the swellest thing.
32. The shrew scolded, while her spouse sat in the garden with the other loafers.
33. He is a good sprinter, in the foot-races.
34. Will you please speak to my hubby about it?
35. Step lively there; hop on, now!
36. I want you to meet my gentleman friend.

XVII. *Exercises for Muscle Coördination.*

A. Arms overhead. Clasp thumbs. Trunk forward and downward bend without bending the knees. Arms straight.

B. Weight on right side, extend right arm high overhead, and stretch, as though picking grapes, above. Repeat to left side.

C. Finer grace movements, including elemental actions of the hands and feet.

D. 1. Hands.
   Simply and naturally extend the hand as tho making the following gestures or actions.
   a. Offer a gift. b. accept, a small article.

      c. Reject a proffered article. d. Conceal something.

      e. Reveal (with wide open hand extended).

      f. Attest to the truth of a statement.

      g. Affirm very positively, "Roosevelt" fashion.

      h. Deny (using arm), and active hand movement.

2. Feet.

      a. Stand with weight evenly balanced over both feet.

      b. With one foot slightly in advance of the other, transfer weight to forward foot. Think of yourself as standing in attention, and animation.

      c. Transfer weight back to back foot, and think of yourself as standing at ease.

      d. Transfer weight until it is evenly distributed between forward and back foot; think of yourself as in hesitation, or uncertainty.

      e. Recoil quickly bringing weight to back foot.

      f. Forward quickly in "explosion", as tho greatly agitated by some accident or the like.

In trying the above exercises work for steady, controlled movements. Avoid jerky, awkward, spasmodic action. Seek for complete, not partial or unfinished movements.

3. Facial muscles of expression.

      Work for emotional variety by thinking of situations which call forth the following responses, in facial expression; pain, pleasure, joy, surprise, grief, fear, courage, contempt, disgust, irony, happiness, laughter.

Note: One should occasionaly test his mental attainment in the following processes:—

Memory, (Ability to acquire; to retain; to recall.)

Logical thinking. (Ability to use logic or judgment.)

Imagination. (Creative instinct; enjoyment of arts, poetry, music, etc.)

Concentration. (Attention to work in hand: fixity of purpose.)

Reasoning. Two courses of action suggested. Which do you choose and why?

XVIII. *The Expressive Coördinations of Body and Voice.*

Posture involves what has been called "manual behavior", whereas speech involves "verbalized" behavior, a more highly specialized process, involving fine muscle coördinations and delicate adjustments. One may be quite unconscious of the fact that he has acquired poor posture habits and poor speech reactions, so firmly have they become fixed and set in his motor mechanism. It is only when a rude awakening comes, through a criticism of the kind received by public men, actors, singers and other artists who appear in public, that the individual becomes suddenly aware of his shortcomings. It may be his manner of talking, walking, or dancing, which is criticised. The hopeful thing about education is, that one may replace such undesirable habits as these when subjected to criticism, first by observation of one's reactions, and then by consciously seeking to replace them by desirable types of reaction. The first step in the process, is to "right about face", to admit that one *DOES* stand poorly, walk ungracefully, or speak in an ineffective way. Next, by application of the principles of learning, one may *undo old habits* and *build up new ones.* This may require some time, but it can be done successfully—it is done on the stage every day, and in the concert hall, occasionally even in the business office and in the drawing room. Speech has been with us so long, that we are often quite unaware of our bad habits with our own language. In learning to talk well, to speak clearly and distinctly, one of the first bits of preparation which the actor must make, is to *stand* properly, and to move harmoniously in the character he wishes to represent upon the stage.

Physical training is not merely intended to be a "setting-up" exercise but a BUILDING UP exercise, to improve general health and hygiene. By deep breathing, daily relaxation and proper food habits, we may add years to our lives, according to the statisticians of some of the insurance companies in this country. With exercise the muscle texture becomes firmer, the will and mind become more attentive, mental alertness and the feeling of well-being pervades us. One is able to maintain a more graceful, self-assured attitude because he is more at ease and more in tune with his surroundings. An easy, graceful carriage, free from jerky unrhythmic movements should be natural to every individual. We see it in the independent mountaineer, the powerful lumber-jack, the circus rider and various athletes who have developed skilful muscle control and dexterity of special muscles. Why should it not be desirable for each of us?

One's bearing should be such as to express controlled, well-directed movements, assured and easy in outward appearance, because wisely and perfectly controlled by an inward power or direction which coördinates these peripheral muscles. We like to think of ourselves as normally "socially adjustive", to feel at home, wherever we are. The degree to which this is expressed in bearing and manner is important to the layman as well as to the actor, or other person in the public eye, because associated with such personality reactions, is his earning capacity, his economic and social success in walks of life.

The exercises outlined here are to assist in the process of self-direction in muscle coördination. We do not perform such exercises in the gymnasium after we leave school, and therefore many of us neglect them entirely. We do have need of constant practise to keep up our skill and rapidity of response, balanced bodily movements, ease and economy of effort in whatever we do, all of the time, and every time, whatever our work or profession.

For practical ends as well as for aesthetic ideals we would recommend the use of such regular progressive gymnastic physical exercise program as one finds in the Swedish system of gymnastics.* It usually includes several of the following, arranged in order of progression.

XIX. *Physical Exercise Program.*

1. Breathing exercises: These are often combined with shoulder blade movements, for chest expansion, use of lower costal muscles and diaphragm in breathing.

*Kinesiology of Special Educational Gymnastics. Baron Nils Posse.

2. Abdominal exercises, to strengthen the muscles and to improve muscle "tonus" or well-being of the muscles which support the viscera.

3. Trunk bending and expansions, to strengthen trunk muscles and for improving the circulation.

4. Slow-leg movements.
a. side-ways; b. forward, c. backward, d. combined. movements front, side and back, in succession.

5. Arm movements for chest expansion and freedom of the shoulders.

6. Head flexions and extension. Also use rotation of head to improve tonus of neck muscles and to assist in maintaining an erect, upright carriage of the head.

XX. *Exercises in Spontaneous Speech.*

A. Take some well-known picture, or a picture in the room in which you are sitting. Ask questions about the story which the picture tells, or have the child make up a story about it. The child may prefer to tell you what he sees in the picture, or to describe it. Let him do so, but do not allow him to interrupt you, or try to begin while you are speaking. Many stutterers do this unconsciously, as they can start more easily while other sounds are going on in the room. It serves to distract their attention from themselves and from their SPEECH DIFFICULTY. They must therefore learn to face the difficulty and overcome it, not to seek to HIDE it.

B. Hold a mock telephone conversation. The topic doesn't matter.

C. Pretend to transact business at a store.

D. Tell a short funny story, or read one and then retell it.

E. Tell a story of some adventure of your own.

F. Put the following words into sentences: book, house, table, home, New Year, Christmas, birthday, school house, dog, cat, pet, quarrel, candy, dinner, party, automobile, bicycle, bowl, chum.

G. Tell the story of some play you have recently seen or of some drama which you have read.

H. Repeat a fable.

I. Tell the story of some book you have recently read.

J. Explain the difference between the construction of a hydroplane and an aeroplane.

K. Tell the story of the rescue of Nobile, the Arctic Explorer after the wreck of the airship "Italia" in the Arctic lands.

L. Describe some trip you have recently taken or an interesting visit to some unusual place, museum, home, cathedral, theatre, etc.

XXI. *Attend Some Public Lecture, Sermon or Other Address, and Classify the Speech Given According to the Following Analysis Blank.*

Speech Analysis Blank.*

Filled out by...................... Date ....

*O'Neill's Modern Speeches. Used by courtesy of J. M. O'Neill, University of Michigan.

Classification.	Plane		Real audience			General end					Form of outline			Form of composition				Form of delivery			Remarks.
	Utility	Art	Hearers only	Readers only	Both.	Instruction	Relief	Action	Impressiveness	Entertainment	Topical	Logical	Chronological	Descriptive	Narrative	Expository	Argumentative	Reading	Memoriter	Extemporaneous	
I. Forensic.																					
II. Deliberative.																					
A. Legislative.																					
B. Campaign.																					
III. Pulpit.																					
IV. Lecture.																					
V. Demonstrative.																					
A. Eulogy.																					
B. Commemorative.																					
1. Dedicatory.																					
2. Anniversary.																					
C. After Dinner.																					
D. Occasional.																					
1. Welcome.																					
2. Farewell.																					
3. Presentation.																					
4. Acceptance.																					
5. Introduction.																					

Subject of thesis _____

Speaker _____

Speech Record Card

Name........................ Home address.............. Date....... Exam. by......

Sex........ Language spoken in home.......... Local address.................. Phone..........

Referred by....................................

I.

Speech diagnosis................(underline) if any of the following: stuttering, oral inaccuracy, lisping, vocal defect, aphonia, aphasia, delayed speech, mutism, cleft palate speech, paralysis affecting vocal cords or other speech organs. Degree of same (underline) mild, moderate, severe.

II. Prognosis.........................

Special drill or treatment recommended................

Results during period of treatment and date when reported...............

....

III. Scholastic record.

Class or grade.......... School or college........... Dates attended...........

School progress (satisfactory, unsatisfactory, grades repeated............

grades skipped)................... Special promotions or other data............

Special interests and ambitions.......................

Means taken to realize same.......................... Rank in class............

IV. Psychological record.

Dates............

Name of test............ Results......... Date.............

Name of test............ Results......... Date.............

Rank in class or grade in tests............ Mental age............. I. Q...........

Chronological age...............

V. Special tests. A. Speech.*

Scores in Articulation test A.............. Test B.............(first trial).

Scores in Oral Reading rate............. Silent reading rate..............

Scores in spontaneous speech (rate)............Score for percentage of relevant words used in

spontaneous speech................................ Vocabulary........................ Speech index..............
Subjective speech rating............... Objective speech rating............. Speech index..............
(Retests may be given from time to time, to check improvement and note any change in scores such
as Articulation, rate in oral and silent reading, increase in vocabulary, and the like.)

B. Emotional traits, tests and reactions.

(Tests suggested for obtaining these reactions, are as follows:—)
1. Pressey-Pressey X-O test of the emotions (complex indicators or significant reactions occurring)
....
2. Woodworth-Wells questionnaire ....
3. Wells-Mathews (yes-no) test ....
4. Association test (such as Kent-Rosanoff, White, Jung, etc.)......................................
(record significant complex indicators, and words on which there was blocking or delay, change of response on second trial, or unusual answer) ....
5. Miscellaneous information from various sources, school, home, associate..........................
....

C. Specific sounds or sound groups and symbols of same, which are difficult;
time taken for their elimination or improvement.

....
....

D. Physical examination or medical records.

Recommendations made by physician, director of physical education department, or other health official
in regard to patient ....
Treatment or help received from the above departments..
Recommendations or requests from other teachers in regard to same..................................
Remarks ....
Follow up records after treatment ceases..
*Scores according to the Blanton-Stinchfield speech tests. See Manual, No. 46087 in this test series.

C. H. Stoelting Co., Chicago, Publishers.

XXII. *Prepare Two of the Following Speeches, As for a Special Occasion.*

1. The speech of introduction (such as introducing the speaker of the evening).
2. Address at a woman's club on current events or special topic.
3. Address of welcome to a visitor from another city or country.
4. Presentation speech: (statue for public park, picture of school, etc.).
5. Speech of acceptance.
6. Patriotic speech (3 minutes); Nomination speech for public official.
7. After-dinner speech.

INDEX

253